Complete
Mathematics
for Cambridge IGCSE®

Fourth edition

Revision Guide

For the updated syllabus

David Rayner
Paul Williams

Oxford excellence for Cambridge IGCSE®

Great Clarendon Street, Oxford, OX2 6DP, United Kingdom

Oxford University Press is a department of the University of Oxford.
It furthers the University's objective of excellence in research,
scholarship, and education by publishing worldwide. Oxford is
a registered trademark of Oxford University Press in the UK and
in certain other countries

British Library Cataloguing in Publication Data

Data available

ISBN: 978-0-19-837839-6
10 9 8 7 6 5 4 3 2

Printed in India by Manipal Technologies Limited

Acknowledgements

® IGCSE is the registered trademark of Cambridge International Examinations.

The publisher would like to thank Cambridge International Examinations for
their kind permission to reproduce past paper questions.

Cambridge International Examinations bears no responsibility for the example
answers to questions taken from its past question papers which are contained
in this publication.

Cover photo by Phaif/Dreamstime

Paper used in the production of this book is a natural, recyclable product made
from wood grown in sustainable forests. The manufacturing process conforms
to the environmental regulations of the country of origin.

Contents

1 Numbers

Sets of numbers

Natural numbers are the numbers you use to count.
So the natural numbers are 1, 2, 3, 4,....

Integers are "whole numbers". They can be positive, or negative (with zero in between).
So the integers are the numbers ...−3, −2, −1, 0, 1, 2, 3...
Positive integers are the numbers 1, 2, 3, 4,...
Negative integers are the numbers −1, −2, −3, −4,...

Sometimes 0 is included with the natural numbers.

Factor Any number which divides into 6 is a factor of 6.
So the factors of 6 are 1, 2, 3, and 6.

Multiple Any number which appears in the 6 times table is a multiple of 6.
So the multiples of 6 are 6, 12, 18, 24,...

Prime numbers A prime number has only two (different) factors (i.e. 1 and itself).
So 1 is not a prime number. The prime numbers are 2, 3, 5, 7, 11, 13, 17, 19...
(The number of primes is infinite).

Prime factor A prime factor is a factor which is also prime.
The factors of 63 are 1, 3, 7, 9, 21 and 63. Of these only 3 and 7 are prime so the prime factors of 63 are 3 and 7.

Arjun has 7 square building blocks. The only way he can make a rectangle with these blocks is to put them in a single straight line because 7 is prime.

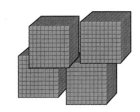

If Arjun has 12 square building blocks then he can make three different rectangles, since 12 is not a prime number.

For example he can make a 3 × 4 rectangle or a 2 × 6 rectangle as well as the 1 × 12 rectangle.

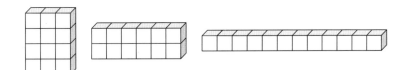

Square numbers
If Arjun has 4 building blocks then he can arrange them in a square (that is a 2 × 2 square). In the same way he can arrange squares of 9, 16, 25... building blocks.
The square numbers are 1, 4, 9, 16...

1 = 1 × 1   4 = 2 × 2   9 = 3 × 3

Common factor 3 is a common factor of 9 and 12 since 3 is a factor of both 9 and 12.

Common multiple 30 is a common multiple of 6 and 15 since 30 is a multiple of both 6 and 15.

Exam question
CIE 0580 November '05 Paper 1 Q10

An integer *n* is such that 60 ⩽ *n* ⩽ 70. Write down *a* value of *n* which is
(a) a prime number
(b) a multiple of 9
(c) a square number.

    (a) 61 and 67 are both prime.
    (b) 63 is the only multiple of 9 between 60 and 70.
    (c) 64 is the only square number between 60 and 70 since 64 = 8 × 8.

Highest common factor (HCF) The highest common factor of 12 and 15 is the largest number which is a factor of both 12 and 15.
The factors of 12 are 1, 2, 3, 4, 6 and 12.
The factors of 15 are 1, 3, 5 and 15.

So 3 is the HCF of 12 and 15.

Lowest common multiple (LCM) The lowest common multiple of 12 and 15 is the smallest number which is a multiple of both 12 and 15.
The multiples of 12 are 12, 24, 36, 48, 60…
The multiples of 15 are 15, 30, 45, 60…

So 60 is the LCM of 12 and 15.

Expressing a number as the product of its prime factors

Example
Express 504 as the product of its prime factors.

    Divide 504 by the lowest possible prime, that is 2.
    Write 504 = 2 × 252
    Divide 252 by the lowest possible prime, that is 2.
    Write 252 = 2 × 126 and so 504 = 2^2 × 126
    Divide 126 by the lowest possible prime, that is 2.
    Write 126 = 2 × 63 and so 504 = 2^3 × 63
    Divide 63 by the lowest possible prime, that is 3.
    Write 63 = 3 × 21 and so 504 = 2^3 × 3 × 21
    Divide 21 by the lowest possible prime, that is 3.
    Write 21 = 3 × 7 and so 504 = 2^3 × 3^2 × 7

504 = 2^3 × 3^2 × 7

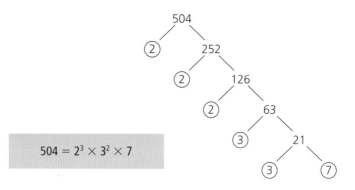

Finding HCFs and LCMs of larger numbers

Example
Find the HCF of 60 and 504.
- **Find the largest power of each prime factor common to both numbers.**
- **Multiply these powers of primes together.**

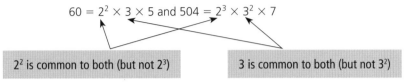

$$60 = 2^2 \times 3 \times 5 \text{ and } 504 = 2^3 \times 3^2 \times 7$$

2^2 is common to both (but not 2^3)   3 is common to both (but not 3^2)

So the highest common factor of 60 and 504 = $2^2 \times 3 = 12$

Example
Find the LCM of 60 and 504.
- **Find the largest power of each prime factor that appears in either number.**
- **Multiply these powers of primes together.**

$$60 = 2^2 \times 3 \times 5 \text{ and } 504 = 2^3 \times 3^2 \times 7$$

2^3 is the largest power of 2 that appears in either expression.
3^2 is the largest power of 3 that appears in either expression.
5 is the largest power of 5 that appears in either expression.
7 is the largest power of 7 that appears in either expression.
So the LCM of 60 and 504 = $2^3 \times 3^2 \times 5 \times 7 = 2520$

Rational and irrational numbers

A **rational number** is a number which can be expressed in the form $\frac{p}{q}$ where p and q are whole numbers.

- All decimals which recur are rational. For example, $0.\dot{3} = 0.333333\ldots$ is rational since $0.\dot{3} = \frac{1}{3}$.
- All decimals which terminate (i.e. which end) are rational. For example, 0.625 is a rational number since 0.625 can be written as $\frac{625}{1000} = \frac{5}{8}$.

$\sqrt{2\frac{1}{4}}$ doesn't look rational but it is since $\sqrt{2\frac{1}{4}} = \sqrt{\frac{9}{4}} = \frac{3}{2}$.

$-2 \qquad 0.\dot{3}$
$-\frac{2}{3} \qquad \frac{5}{12} \qquad 0.7\dot{2}\dot{5}$
$13 \qquad \frac{3}{4}$
$\sqrt{\frac{4}{9}} = \frac{2}{3}$

An **irrational number** is a number which *cannot* be expressed in the form $\frac{p}{q}$ where p and q are integers.

For example π, $\sqrt{2}$ and $\sqrt[3]{7}$ are all irrational numbers.

$\sqrt{3}$, $\sqrt{5}$, $\sqrt{27}$ etc. are all irrational.
But be careful: $\sqrt{36}$ is rational since $\sqrt{36} = 6 = \frac{6}{1}$.

$\pi \qquad \sqrt{3}$
$-\sqrt{2} \qquad \frac{\pi}{4} \qquad \pi + 1$
$\sqrt{5} + \sqrt{7} \qquad \frac{\sqrt[3]{3}}{2}$

A **real number** is a number which can be represented on the number line.

All the numbers used in IGCSE are real numbers (e.g. π, $\sqrt{2}$, $\frac{1}{2}$, -3).

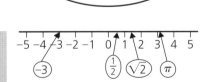

Exam question

CIE 0580 June '08 Paper 1 Q20

$$\sqrt{4} \quad \sqrt{14} \quad \sqrt{36} \quad \sqrt{64} \quad \sqrt{81} \quad \sqrt{100}$$

From the list above, write down

(a) a prime number

(b) a factor of 27

(c) a multiple of 4

(d) an irrational number.

(a) prime number is $\sqrt{4} = 2$

(b) factor of 27 is $\sqrt{81} = 9$

(c) multiple of 4 is $\sqrt{64} = 8$

(d) an irrational number is $\sqrt{14}$

Questions

1. Which of these numbers is **not** a rational number?

$$\frac{3}{5} \quad \sqrt{7} \quad 0.6 \quad -1\frac{2}{3} \quad \sqrt{25}$$

2. An integer n is such that $80 \leqslant n < 90$.
Write down a value of n which is:
(a) a multiple of both 3 and 4
(b) a prime number
(c) a factor of 1700.

3. Find:
(a) a prime number which is a factor of 49
(b) an even prime number.

4. (a) Write down all the factors of 21.
(b) Write down all the factors of 28.
(c) Hence find the HCF of 21 and 28.

5. $\sqrt{9} \quad \sqrt{15} \quad \sqrt{49} \quad \sqrt{16} \quad \sqrt{64}$
$\sqrt{121}$
From the list above, write down
(a) a prime number less than 10

(b) a factor of 22
(c) a power of 2
(d) an irrational number.

6. Write each number as the product of prime factors
(e.g. $72 = 2^3 \times 3^2$).
(a) 30   (b) 24
(c) 18   (d) 28
(e) 105   (f) 64

7. Use question 6 to find the highest common factor of each pair of numbers.
(a) 30 and 24
(b) 28 and 64
(c) 18 and 105

8. Use question 6 to find the lowest common multiple of each pair of numbers.
(a) 30 and 64
(b) 24 and 105
(c) 28 and 18

2 Sequences

A sequence is a set of numbers which follows a certain pattern.
For example suppose a collection of matchsticks is arranged to make squares as shown.

The number of matchsticks used is 4 in the first pattern, then 7 in the second, then 10, then 13. You could write this sequence as 4, 7, 10, 13,…

The word "term" is used to refer to the various numbers in a sequence.

The first term, t_1, is 4.
The second term, t_2, is 7, and so on. The notation t_n represents the nth term.
The terms 4, 7, 10, 13,… are all 1 greater than the corresponding multiple of 3 so:

$$
\begin{aligned}
\textbf{1}\text{st term} &= 4 &&= 3 \times \textbf{1} + 1 \\
\textbf{2}\text{nd term} &= 7 &&= 3 \times \textbf{2} + 1 \\
\textbf{3}\text{rd term} &= 10 &&= 3 \times \textbf{3} + 1 \\
\textbf{4}\text{th term} &= 13 &&= 3 \times \textbf{4} + 1
\end{aligned}
$$

The pattern here can be seen and so we write nth term, $t_n = 3 \times n + 1 = 3n + 1$

Sequences with the same difference between terms

The pattern in the sequence 4, 7, 10, 13,… is that the next term is always three more than the previous one. So the difference between consecutive terms is always the same.

There is a simple way to find the nth term in sequences like these.

The nth term of such sequences is $t_n = an + b$

The constants a and b need to be found.
The easiest way to find a and b is as follows:

If the sequence is extended backwards, then the number that appears before the first term is b.

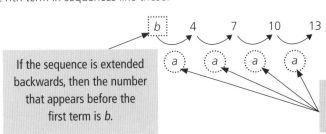

The difference between consecutive terms is a.

In this case $a = 3$ and $b = 1$. So $t_n = an + b = 3n + 1$

Example
(a) What is the nth term of 19, 13, 7, 1,…?
(b) Which term of 19, 13, 7, 1,… is equal to −47?

(a) The differences are all −6.
So the nth term is $-6n + 25$
which can be written as $25 - 6n$.

If the sequence is extended backwards, then the number that appears before the first term is 25.

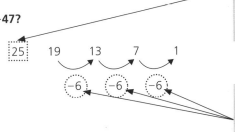

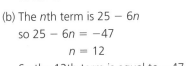

The difference between consecutive terms is −6.

(b) The nth term is $25 - 6n$
so $25 - 6n = -47$
$n = 12$
So the 12th term is equal to −47.

Sequences with the same ratio between terms

In the sequences above there is the same *difference* between consecutive terms.
These are other sequences in which there is the same *ratio* between consecutive terms.

Example

Find the next two terms of the sequence 3, 6, 12, 24, 48…

Each term is double the previous term:

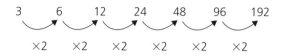

So the next two terms are 96 and 192.

Using the notation t_n to represent the nth term, you can write $t_1 = 3$, $t_2 = 6$,… and then say that $t_n = 2t_{n-1}$ since the nth term is twice the $(n-1)$th term.

Example

Find the first three terms of the sequence in which $t_1 = 5$ and $t_n = 3t_{n-1}$.

In this sequence the first term is 5 and each subsequent term is three times the previous term.

So the sequence is 5, 15, 45, 135,…

Other sequences

Here are some well-known sequences:

Prime numbers 2, 3, 5, 7, 11, 13, 17, 19,… (there is no relationship between the differences of consecutive terms)

Square numbers 1, 4, 9, 16, 25… (difference between terms increases by 2 each time)

Triangular numbers 1, 3, 6, 10, 15…. (difference between terms increases by 1 each time)

Fibonacci numbers The sequence 1, 1, 2, 3, 5, 8, 13,… is known as the Fibonacci sequence. The first two terms are both 1 and then each term is obtained by adding the two previous terms. The sequence has some interesting properties. For example in many plants the number of petals is a term from the Fibonacci sequence (buttercups have 5 petals).

Example

The nth term of a sequence is given by $n^2 - 1$. Find the fifth term.

Replace the n by 5 to give $5^2 - 1 = 24$

Exam question   CIE 0580 November '05 Paper 2 Q4

Write down the next two terms in each of the following sequences:

  (a) 8.2, 6.2, 4.2, 2.2, 0.2, …

  (b) 1, 3, 6, 10, 15, …

(a)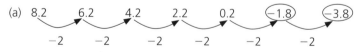

The next two terms are −1.8 and −3.8.

(b)

The next two terms are 21 and 28.

Extended

Exam question

CIE 0580 June '08 Paper 2 Q4

(a) The formula for the nth term of the sequence

$$1, 5, 14, 30, 55, 91, \ldots \text{ is } \frac{n(n + 1)(2n + 1)}{6}.$$

Find the 20th term.

(b) The nth term of the sequence 10, 17, 26, 37, 50, ... is $(n + 2)^2 + 1$.
Write down the formula for the nth term of the sequence
17, 26, 37, 50, 65,...

(a) Replacing n with 20 gives $\dfrac{20 \times 21 \times 41}{6} = 2870$

(b) $10 = \mathbf{3}^2 + 1$ $17 = \mathbf{4}^2 + 1$ $26 = \mathbf{5}^2 + 1$ etc.

The nth term of $\mathbf{3}$, $\mathbf{4}$, $\mathbf{5}$,... is $n + 2$ so the nth term of 10, 17, 26,...
is $(n + 2)^2 + 1$
$17 = \mathbf{4}^2 + 1$ $26 = \mathbf{5}^2 + 1$ $37 = \mathbf{6}^2 + 1$ etc.

The nth term of $\mathbf{4}$, $\mathbf{5}$, $\mathbf{6}$,... is $n + 3$ (using method shown earlier) so the nth
term of 17, 26, 37, 50, 65,... $(n + 3)^2 + 1$.

Questions

1. A football club has 35 000 supporters at its first home
match. The attendance increases by 250 at each home
game.
(a) How many supporters will be at the nth home game?
(b) If there are 37 750 at the last home game of the
season then how many home games did the club
play?

2. Joshua decides to save money in the following way:
He saves £1 in the first week, £1.20 in the second
week, £1.40 in the third week, and so on.
(a) How much would he save in the nth week?
(b) How much would he save in the 8th week?
(c) In which week would he first save at least £5?
(d) After 10 weeks, Joshua wants to buy a tennis racquet
which costs £19.99. He realises that he hasn't saved
quite enough, but by how much is he short?

3. Find the first three terms in a sequence whose nth term is:
(a) $5n - 1$ (b) $n^2 - 1$
(c) $\frac{1}{2} n (n + 1)$ (d) $\dfrac{n^3 + 1}{3n}$

4. Find the next two terms in each sequence.
(a) 5, 10, 20, 40, 80,...
(b) 1, 8, 27, 64, 125,...
(c) 2, 8, 18, 32, 50,...
(d) $\dfrac{3}{4}, \dfrac{5}{9}, \dfrac{7}{16}, \dfrac{9}{25}, \dfrac{11}{36}, \ldots$

5. The diagrams shows a sequence of regular
pentagons. Sticks of equal length are used
to make the pentagons.

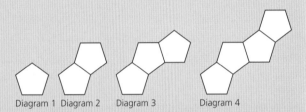

Diagram 1   Diagram 2   Diagram 3   Diagram 4

(a) Copy and complete the table for the number of
sticks in each diagram.

Diagram	1	2	3	4	5
Sticks	5	9			

(b) How many sticks are in the 25th diagram?
(c) How many stick are in the nth diagram?
(d) How many pentagons are in the diagram with
129 sticks?

6. Find the next term in each sequence:
(a) 4, 12, 36, 108, 324...
(b) 3, 8, 11, 19, 30...
(c) 6, 8, 11, 15, 20...
(d) $3x^2, 6x^3, 12x^4, 24x^5, \ldots$

7. The number of golf balls (G) in this diagram is given by
the formula $G = \frac{1}{2} n (n+1)$, where n is the number of
rows. There are 4 rows in the diagram. How many golf
balls will there be in a diagram with 15 rows?

3 Sets

A set is a collection of items – such as numbers, people, letters etc.

For example

Set *A* is the set of pupils in year 11 who wear glasses.

Set *B* is the set of pupils in year 11 who have blonde hair.

An element is an individual item of a set, for example a particular pupil in year 11 is an element.

Venn diagrams

Venn diagrams can be used to represent sets.

A Venn diagram consists of a large rectangle with circles or ovals inside to represent the various sets.

The circles may or may not overlap.

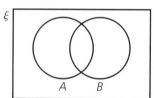

The symbol ℰ beside the rectangle represents "the universal set". This might be, for example, all year 11 pupils. In this example only year 11 pupils in this school would feature in the Venn diagram.

If an element is in set *A* and also in set *B* then it lies in the intersection of the two circles.

If an element is neither in *A* nor *B* then it lies inside the rectangle but outside both circles.

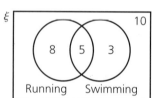

Example

The Venn diagram shows students in a class who enjoy swimming and running.

(a) How many students enjoy both running and swimming?

(b) How many enjoy running?

(c) How many enjoy neither running nor swimming?

> (a) There are 5 students who enjoy both running and swimming as there are 5 students lying in the intersection of the two circles.
>
> (b) There are 13 who enjoy running. That is the 8 who enjoy running but not swimming and the 5 who enjoy both running and swimming.
>
> (c) There are 10 students who enjoy neither running nor swimming. These are the 10 who lie outside both circles.

Example

In a class of 33 students, 20 like chess, 12 like draughts and 5 like neither. Represent this on a Venn diagram.

> Those who like chess will be represented by one circle, those who like draughts will be represented by another circle. Those who like both are in the overlap of the circles while those who like neither will lie outside both circles.

So the 5 who like neither go outside the two circles.

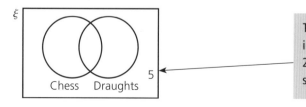

These 5 students do not lie in either circle so that leaves 28 to be put in the three spaces inside the circles.

How is the rest of the Venn diagram to be filled in?

The two circles can overlap. Imagine that one circle has total 20 (students who like chess), one has total 12 (students who like draughts). The combined total has to be 28.

If the circles did not overlap their combined total would be 32 (20 + 12) so the overlap must have 4 (32 − 28).

There are 20 altogether who like chess so 16 must go in here.

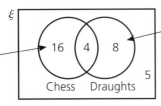

There are 12 altogether who like draughts so 8 must go in here.

Set notation

If set A is the set of even numbers less than 10 then

$$A = \{2, 4, 6, 8\}$$

> The members or elements of set A are listed inside curly brackets.

$4 \in A$ means that 4 is an element of A.
$9 \notin A$ means that 9 is *not* an element of A.
$n(A)$ represents the number of elements in A. If $A = \{2, 4, 6, 8\}$ then $n(A) = 4$.

$A \cup B$ means the union of sets A and B, that is, all the elements which belong to A or B or *both*.

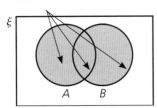

$A \cap B$ means the intersection of sets A and B, that is, only the elements which belong to both A *and* B.

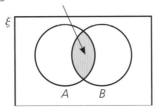

$A \subset B$ means that A is a **proper** subset of B.

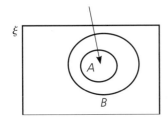

A' (called the complement of A) represents all the elements that are not in A.

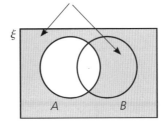

> The shaded area represents A'.

NB When A is a subset of B, $A \cup B = B$.
$A \not\subset B$ means that A is not a proper subset of B.
$A \subset B$ means that A lies inside B but A cannot be equal to B.
$A \subseteq B$ means that A lies inside B but A can be equal to B.

The empty set $\varnothing$ or { } are the symbols used for "the empty set" so $A \cap B = \varnothing$ if there is no element that belongs both to A and B.

Extended

For example if ℰ is the set of polygons, set A is quadrilaterals and set B is triangles then the Venn diagram would look like this:

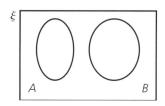

In this example $A \cap B = \varnothing$ since a polygon cannot be a quadrilateral and a triangle. The two ovals do not intersect.

Example

ℰ is all whole numbers less than 10.

A = {x : x is an even number}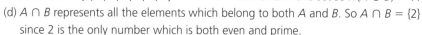

B = {x : x is a prime number}

(a) Express this on a Venn diagram.

(b) List all the elements of A′.

(c) What is n(A ∪ B)?

(d) Find A ∩ B.

This notation means that A consists of all numbers x, where x is an even number.

(a) Since ℰ is all whole numbers less than 10, the only numbers appearing on the Venn diagram are 1, 2, 3, 4, 5, 6, 7, 8 and 9.

(b) A′ contains all the elements outside A. So A′ = {1, 3, 5, 7, 9}

(c) A ∪ B represents all the elements which belong to A or B or *both*.

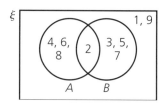

So A ∪ B = {2, 3, 4, 5, 6, 7, 8}. There are 7 elements in this set so n(A ∪ B) = 7.

(d) A ∩ B represents all the elements which belong to both A and B. So A ∩ B = {2} since 2 is the only number which is both even and prime.

Shading unions

Example

A′ ∪ B includes any region that is shaded in A′ or B (or both).

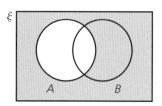

A′ is shaded

∪

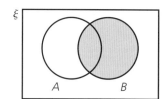

B is shaded

=

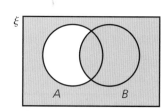

A′ ∪ B is shaded

Example

A′ ∪ B′ includes any region that is shaded in A′ or B′ (or both).

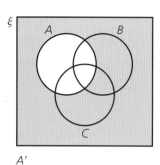

A′

∪

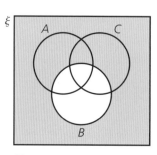

B′

=

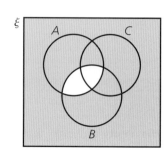

A′ ∪ B′

Extended

Shading intersections

Example

A′ ∩ B includes any region that is shaded in both *A′* and *B*.

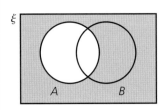 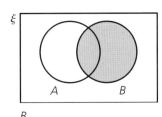 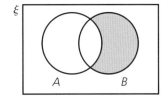

A′   *B*   *A′ ∩ B*

Example

A′ ∩ B′ includes any region that is shaded in both *A′* and *B′*.

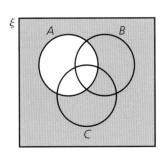 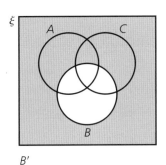 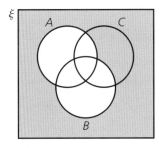

A′   *B′*   *A′ ∩ B′*

Exam question
CIE 0580 November '05 Paper 4 Q4 a

All 24 students in a class are asked whether they like football and whether they like basketball. Some of the results are shown in the Venn diagram below.

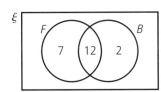

ℰ = {students in the class}.
F = {students who like football}.
B = {students who like basketball}.

(a) How many students like both sports?
(b) How many students like neither sport?
(c) Write down the value of $n(F \cup B)$.
(d) Write down the value of $n(F' \cap B)$.
(e) A student from the class is selected at random. What is the probability that this student likes basketball?
(f) A student who likes football is selected at random. What is the probability that this student likes basketball?

(a) The 12 people in the intersection of the two ovals like both sports.
(b) The diagram has numbers in three of the four regions. The total number of students in the three regions is 7 + 12 + 2 = 21. There are 24 students in the class so that leaves 3 students who are in the fourth region, which is those who like neither sport.

(Continued)

Exam question (Continued)

(c) $F \cup B$ represents those who like football or basketball or both. There are $7 + 12 + 2$ $= 21$ in this region so $n(F \cup B) = 21$.

(d) $F' \cap B$ represents those who do not like football but who do like basketball.

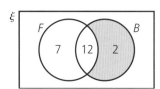

So $n(F' \cap B) = 2$

(e) $12 + 2 = 14$ students like basketball out of 24 students in the class. So probability is $\frac{14}{24} = \frac{7}{12}$.

(f) $7 + 12 = 19$ students like football. Of those 12 like basketball. So probability is $\frac{12}{19}$.

Questions

1. Describe the shaded regions:

(a)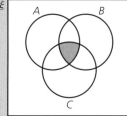

(b)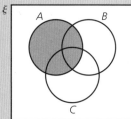

(c)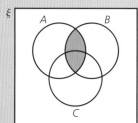

(d)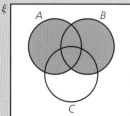

2. In a year of 100 students, 70 enjoy Maths, 50 enjoy French and 20 enjoy neither.
(a) Draw a Venn diagram showing this information.
(b) Use your diagram to find the number of students who enjoy both subjects.

3. In a shop there were 120 customers on a certain day. Of these 60 paid using notes, 30 paid using coins and 50 paid using cards.
(a) Draw a Venn diagram showing this information.
(b) Use your diagram to find the number of customers who used both notes and coins.

4. On an athletics day 150 athletes take part. 60 are in the 100 metres, 50 are in the 200 metres and 80 are in neither.
(a) Draw a Venn diagram showing this information.
(b) Use the diagram to find the number of athletes who ran in only one race.

4 Calculations

The **square** of a number n is $n \times n = n^2$, so the square of 5 is $5^2 = 25$

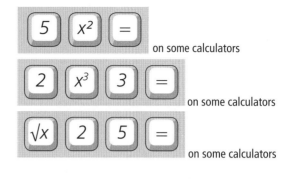

on some calculators

The **cube** of a number n is $n \times n \times n = n^3$, so the cube of 2 is $2^3 = 8$

on some calculators

$25 = 5^2$
5 is the **square root** of 25.
The square root of n is represented by $\sqrt{n}$.
So $\sqrt{25} = 5$

on some calculators

$8 = 2^3$
2 is the **cube root** of 8. The cube root of n is represented by $\sqrt[3]{n}$.
So $\sqrt[3]{8} = 2$

on some calculators

Exam question
CIE 0580 June '06 Paper 1 Q5

A cube of side l metres has a volume of 20 cubic metres. Calculate the value of l.

l m

l m

l m

$l^3 = 20$
$l = \sqrt[3]{20}$
$l = 2.71$ m (to 3 sf)

> Calculators are not all the same. Learn how yours works.

Order of calculations

James first calculates "three plus five" to give $3 + 5 = 8$ and then does "times by two" to give $8 \times 2 = 16$.

> What is two times three plus five?

Akshay first calculates "two times three" to give $2 \times 3 = 6$ and then does "plus five" to give $6 + 5 = 11$.

When calculating expressions with several operations you have to do the working in the right order. The order is:

Brackets – for example $(3 + 4)$
Indices – for example 2^3 or $\sqrt{3}$
Division – for example $8 \div 2$ → **BIDMAS**
Multiplication – for example 3×4
Addition – for example $5 + 2$
Subtraction – for example $7 - 2$

Without a calculator

Example
Calculate $(3 + 4)^2 \times 3 + (5 + 7) \div 6 - 1$

Using the B of BIDMAS gives $(3 + 4)^2 \times 3 + (5 + 7) \div 6 - 1 = 7^2 \times 3 + 12 \div 6 - 1$
Using the I of BIDMAS gives $7^2 \times 3 + 12 \div 6 - 1 = 49 \times 3 + 12 \div 6 - 1$
Using the D of BIDMAS gives $49 \times 3 + 12 \div 6 - 1 = 49 \times 3 + 2 - 1$
Using the M of BIDMAS gives $49 \times 3 + 2 - 1 = 147 + 2 - 1$
Using the A of BIDMAS gives $147 + 2 - 1 = 149 - 1$
Using the S of BIDMAS gives $149 - 1 = 148$

Example

Add brackets to this expression to make the answer correct:

$$4 \times 5 - 3 - 7 = 1$$

Possible positions for the brackets are:

$(4 \times 5) - 3 - 7 = 20 - 3 - 7 = 10$

$4 \times 5 - (3 - 7) = 20 - (-4) = 24$

$4 \times (5 - 3) - 7 = 4 \times 2 - 7 = 1$

So the correct position for the brackets is $4 \times (5 - 3) - 7 = 4 \times 2 - 7 = 1$

With a calculator

The calculator operates using BIDMAS.

If, for example, you type in $7 + 9 \div 3 - 1$

The calculator :

Does the **D**ivision first to give $7 + 3 - 1$

Then the **A**ddition to give $10 - 1$

Then the **S**ubtraction to give 9

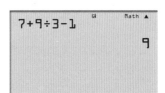

If you want the calculator to work out $\frac{7 + 9}{3 - 1}$ then you type the expression using brackets. Type in $(7 + 9) \div (3 - 1)$ as shown to get the answer 8.

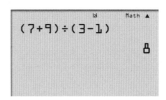

Example

(a) Work out $\sqrt{(7.62 + 8.13)}$, writing down all the figures on your calculator display.

(b) Write the answer to part (a) correct to 2 significant figures.

(a) You must instruct the calculator to work out $\sqrt{(7.62 + 8.13)}$ **not** $\sqrt{7.62} + 8.13$.

Some calculators open brackets automatically when $\boxed{\sqrt{}}$ is pressed. Others may not. Others do not need them as they write everything under the square root.

So type in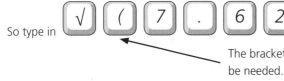

The brackets may appear automatically or may not be needed.

The display might look like this:

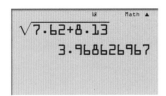

The screen on your calculator might have a different layout.

(b) $\sqrt{(7.62 + 8.13)} = 4.0$ (to 2 sf)

Example

(a) Work out $\frac{5.2 + 4.3}{6.1 - 2.7}$, writing down all the figures on your calculator display.

(b) Write the answer to part (a) correct to 2 significant figures.

(a) It is often safest to calculate the top and bottom of the expressions, write them down *in full* and then do a separate calculation.

$5.2 + 4.3 = 9.5$ and $6.1 - 2.7 = 3.4$

So $\frac{5.2 + 4.3}{6.1 - 2.7} = \frac{9.5}{3.4}$

Typing this into a calculator gives:

$\frac{5.2 + 4.3}{6.1 - 2.7} = 2.794117647$

(b) $\frac{5.2 + 4.3}{6.1 - 2.7} = 2.8$ (to 2 sf)

This calculation can be done in one go on the calculator.

You have to bracket the top expression and bracket the bottom expression. The display looks like this:

```
(5.2+4.3)
(6.1-2.7)
        2.794117647
```

```
9.5÷3.4
        2.794117647
```

Exam question

CIE 0580 June '06 Paper 1 Q6

(a) Work out

$$\frac{12.48 \times 0.063}{\sqrt{8} + 7.52}$$

Write down all the figures on your calculator display.

(b) Write your answer to part (a) correct to 2 significant figures.

(a) Type in $(12.48 \times 0.063) \div (\sqrt{8} + 7.52)$.
The display looks like this:

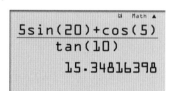

(b) $\dfrac{12.48 \times 0.063}{\sqrt{8} + 7.52} = 0.076$ (to 2 sf)

Using ANS on calculator

If you type in 12.48×0.063 to get 0.78624 and then $\sqrt{8} + 7.52$ to get 10.34842712 (on the calculator display) you can then type

> ⓜ Math ▲
> 0.78624÷Ans
>   0.07597676348

The "Ans" uses the value that the calculator last calculated. In this case $\sqrt{8} + 7.52$

Example

Use your calculator to work out $\dfrac{5 \sin 20° + \cos 5°}{\tan 10°}$**, giving your answer to 3 sf.**

You need to bracket the numerator of this expression or else use the fraction button on some calculators.

The display looks like this:

> ⓜ Math ▲
> $\dfrac{5\sin(20)+\cos(5)}{\tan(10)}$
>   15.34816398

$$\frac{5 \sin 20° + \cos 5°}{\tan 10°} = 15.3 \text{ (to 3 sf)}$$

Questions

1. Find l (to 3 sf) given that the volume of the cube is 50 cm³.

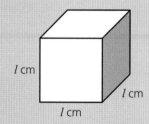

2. Calculate the value of each expression (to 3 sf where necessary):
   (a) 8^2 (b) 11^3 (c) 7.1^2
   (d) $\sqrt{17}$ (e) $\sqrt[3]{-100}$ (f) $\sqrt[3]{6859}$

3. Find the side length of a square whose area is 49 cm².

4. Find the side length of a cube whose volume is 216 cm³.

5. Write the following in ascending order (smallest first):
   (a) 0.6^3 $\sqrt[3]{0.6}$ $\sqrt{0.6}$ 0.6 0.6^2
   (b) 6^3 $\sqrt[3]{6}$ $\sqrt{6}$ 6 6^2

6. Add one set of brackets to each calculation to make it correct.
   (a) $4 + 15 \div 5 - 2 \times 5 = 29$
   (b) $3 + 2^2 \times 3 = 15$
   (c) $5 + 3 \times 2 + 7 = 32$

7. Calculate the value of each expression (to 3 sf).
   (a) $\sqrt{7.2 \times 3.5 + 2.1 \times 5.7}$
   (b) $\dfrac{6.1 - 3.5}{2.1 + 4.7 \times 1.8}$
   (c) $\dfrac{2.7^2 + 4.2^3}{1.9^4}$

5 Directed numbers

You can use a number line to show directed numbers. −5 −4 −3 −2 −1 0 1 2 3 4 5

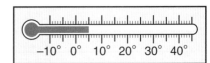

Adding and subtracting

To add a positive number (or subtract a negative number) move to the right on the number line.

Example

(−4) + 6 = 2

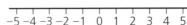

> A move of 6 to the right.

To subtract a positive number (or add a negative number) move to the left.

Example

5 + (−2) = 5 − 2 = 3

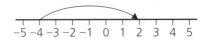

> A move of 2 to the left.

Example

The temperature in Moscow was −1°C at 2300. By 0400 the next day it had fallen by 3°C. What was the temperature at 0400?

The temperature was (−1) − 3 = −4°C

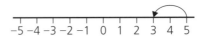

Multiplying and dividing

Multiplying or dividing two negative numbers or two positive numbers gives a positive number.

Multiplying or dividing a negative number and a positive number gives a negative number.

Example

$(−4) \times (−2) = 8$ $3 \times (−5) = −15$

$(−10) \div (−2) = 5$ $(−6) \div 3 = −2$

Exam question
CIE 0580 June '08 Paper 1 Q6

In May, the average temperature in Kiev was 12°C.
In February, the average temperature was 26°C lower than in May.
What was the average temperature in February?

The average temperature in February was 12 − 26 = −14°C

Questions

1. The average temperature each month in Montreal is shown in the table.

Month	Jan	Feb	Mar	Apr	May	Jun
Avg Temp	−11	−9	−3	5	13	18

	Jul	Aug	Sep	Oct	Nov	Dec
	21	19	15	8	1	−7

(a) Find the difference between the highest and lowest average monthly temperatures.

(b) The average minimum temperature for December is usually 5° lower than the average December temperature. Find the average minimum temperature for December.

2. Calculate the following:
(a) 17 + (−3)   (b) (−4) × (−2)
(c) (−7) − (−1)   (d) 15 − (−4)
(e) (−18) ÷ (−3)   (f) (−40) ÷ 10

3. A man's bank balance is −£345.20. He then withdraws £50. What is his new balance?

4. The water on a gauge is at −20 cm, that is 20 cm below the flood level. If the water rises by 25 cm what level does the gauge show?

6 Fractions and decimals

Fractions

If a cake is split into five equal pieces and Joe eats one of the five pieces then the amount he eats can be expressed:

as a **fraction**, that is $\frac{1}{5}$ of the whole cake.

as a **decimal**, that is 0.2 of the whole cake. } the three expressions are equal

as a **percentage**, that is 20% of the whole cake.

Fractions

When you write a number as a fraction you write it in the form $\frac{5}{8}$.

5 is the numerator

8 is the denominator

If Ann shades 4 out of 6 equal sectors of a circle then she shades $\frac{4}{6}$ of the circle.

However you can also see that she has shaded $\frac{2}{3}$ of the circle.

So $\frac{2}{3} = \frac{4}{6}$.

When it is 15 minutes after 3 pm, 15 minutes out of 60 minutes in the hour have gone by and the time is a quarter past three.

So $\frac{15}{60} = \frac{1}{4}$

- **Remember** If you multiply or divide the numerator and the denominator of a fraction by the same number then the value of the fraction is not changed.

So, as you saw above, $\overset{\times 2}{\frac{2}{3}} = \frac{4}{6}$ and $\overset{\div 15}{\frac{15}{60}} = \frac{1}{4}$

$\times 2$ $\div 15$

Writing a number in "its lowest form" or "its simplest form" means writing it so that the numerator and denominator do not have any common factors (except 1).

Example

Write $\frac{4}{18}$ in its lowest form.

4 and 18 have a common factor of 2.

$$\frac{4}{18} = \frac{4 \div 2}{18 \div 2} = \frac{2}{9}$$

$\frac{2}{9}$ is the lowest form since 2 and 9 have no common factors (except 1).

Decimals and percentages

In a decimal number the decimal point separates the whole number part from the fractions. The fractions are tenths, hundredths, thousandths and so on.

$$5.73 = 5 + \frac{7}{10} + \frac{3}{100}$$

Example
Express 0.15 as (a) a fraction (b) a percentage.

(a) $0.15 = \frac{1}{10} + \frac{5}{100} = \frac{15}{100} = \frac{3}{20}$ (b) $0.15 = 0.15 \times 100\% = 15\%$

$100\% = \frac{100}{100} = 1$ so if you multiply 0.15 by 100% its value is not changed.

Example

Express the fraction $\frac{2}{5}$ as (a) a decimal (b) a percentage.

(a) $\frac{2}{5} = \frac{4}{10} = 0.4$

(b) $\frac{2}{5} = 0.4 \times 100\% = 40\%$

Example

Write down three equal numbers from this list:

| 0.008 | 8% | 0.8% | $\frac{2}{250}$ | $\frac{8}{100}$ | 0.8 | 800% |

Write all the numbers as decimals.

0.008   8% = 0.08   0.8% = 0.008 $\frac{2}{250} = \frac{8}{1000} = 0.008$

$\frac{8}{100} = 0.08$ 0.8   800% = 8

So the three equal numbers are 0.008, 0.8% and $\frac{2}{250}$.

Addition and subtraction of fractions

- **Same denominators**

  If the fractions have the same denominator then add the two numerators and leave the denominator unchanged.

Example

$\frac{2}{7} + \frac{3}{7}$ $5 = 2 + 3$

$\frac{2}{7} + \frac{3}{7} = \frac{5}{7}$ ← Denominator left unchanged →

Example

$\frac{7}{11} - \frac{4}{11}$ $3 = 7 - 4$

$\frac{7}{11} - \frac{4}{11} = \frac{3}{11}$

- **Different denominators**

  If the fractions have different denominators then rewrite them so that they have the same denominator (the LCM of the denominators).

Example

$\frac{1}{6} + \frac{1}{10}$

LCM of 6 and 10 is 30 so write

$\frac{1}{6}$ as $\frac{5}{30}$ and $\frac{1}{10}$ as $\frac{3}{30}$.

Hence $\frac{1}{6} + \frac{1}{10} = \frac{5}{30} + \frac{3}{30} = \frac{8}{30} = \frac{4}{15}$

Example

$\frac{7}{12} + \frac{5}{18}$

LCM of 12 and 18 is 36 so write

$\frac{7}{12}$ as $\frac{21}{36}$ and $\frac{5}{18}$ as $\frac{10}{36}$.

Hence $\frac{7}{12} + \frac{5}{18} = \frac{21}{36} + \frac{10}{36} = \frac{31}{36}$

- **Mixed numbers**

  A "mixed number" is a number such as $4\frac{3}{5}$. So it is a mixture of a whole number and a fraction.

Example

$5\frac{7}{12} + 7\frac{2}{3}$

> NB Method 1 is simpler when adding or subtracting large numbers.

Method 1

$5\frac{7}{12} + 7\frac{2}{3} = 5 + \frac{7}{12} + 7 + \frac{2}{3}$

$= 12 + \frac{7}{12} + \frac{2}{3}$

$= 12 + \frac{7}{12} + \frac{8}{12}$

$= 12 + \frac{15}{12}$

$= 12 + 1\frac{3}{12}$

$= 13\frac{3}{12}$

$= 13\frac{1}{4}$

Method 2

Write both fractions as "top heavy fractions"

So $5\frac{7}{12} = 5 + \frac{7}{12} = \frac{60}{12} + \frac{7}{12} = \frac{67}{12}$

and $7\frac{2}{3} = 7 + \frac{2}{3} = \frac{21}{3} + \frac{2}{3} = \frac{23}{3}$

So

$5\frac{7}{12} + 7\frac{1}{3} = \frac{67}{12} + \frac{23}{3}$

$= \frac{67}{12} + \frac{92}{12}$

$= \frac{159}{12}$

$= 13\frac{3}{12}$

$= 13\frac{1}{4}$

Example

$6\frac{5}{8} - 3\frac{3}{4}$

Method 1

$$6\frac{5}{8} - 3\frac{3}{4} = 6 + \frac{5}{8} - \left(3 + \frac{3}{4}\right)$$
$$= 6 + \frac{5}{8} - 3 - \frac{3}{4}$$
$$= 6 - 3 + \frac{5}{8} - \frac{3}{4}$$
$$= 3 + \frac{5}{8} - \frac{6}{8}$$
$$= 3 - \frac{1}{8}$$
$$= 2\frac{7}{8}$$

Method 2

Write both fractions as "top heavy fractions"

So $6\frac{5}{8} = 6 + \frac{5}{8} = \frac{48}{8} + \frac{5}{8} = \frac{53}{8}$

and $3\frac{3}{4} = 3 + \frac{3}{4} = \frac{12}{4} + \frac{3}{4} = \frac{15}{4}$

So

$$6\frac{5}{8} - 3\frac{3}{4} = \frac{53}{8} - \frac{15}{4}$$
$$= \frac{53}{8} - \frac{30}{8}$$
$$= \frac{23}{8}$$
$$= 2\frac{7}{8}$$

Multiplication of fractions

- Multiply the numerators together and multiply the denominators together.

Example $\frac{2}{7} \times \frac{3}{5} = \frac{2 \times 3}{7 \times 5} = \frac{6}{35}$

Remember to cancel out common factors.

Example $\frac{7}{11} \times \frac{3}{14} = \frac{\cancel{7}^1}{11} \times \frac{3}{\cancel{14}^2} = \frac{3}{22}$

Example Find $\frac{2}{3}$ of 120.

$$\frac{2}{3} \times 120 = \frac{2}{\cancel{3}} \times \frac{\cancel{120}^{40}}{1}$$
$$= \frac{80}{1} = 80$$

- **Mixed numbers**

   Example

   Find $1\frac{2}{9} \times 2\frac{2}{11}$

   Write both numbers as "top heavy fractions".

   So $1\frac{2}{9} = 1 + \frac{2}{9} = \frac{11}{9}$ and $2\frac{2}{11} = 2 + \frac{2}{11} = \frac{24}{11}$

   So $1\frac{2}{9} \times 2\frac{2}{11} = \frac{\cancel{11}^1}{\cancel{9}^3} \times \frac{\cancel{24}^8}{\cancel{11}^1}$
   $$= \frac{8}{3}$$
   $$= 2\frac{2}{3}$$

Division of fractions

- Write both fractions as top heavy fractions
- "Flip over" the second fraction and change the division sign into a multiplication sign.

Example

Find $3\frac{1}{2} \div 9\frac{1}{3}$

$$3\frac{1}{2} \div 9\frac{1}{3} = \frac{7}{2} \div \frac{28}{3}$$
$$= \frac{7}{2} \times \frac{3}{28}$$
$$= \frac{\cancel{7}^1}{2} \times \frac{3}{\cancel{28}^4}$$
$$= \frac{3}{8}$$

← Write both fractions as top heavy fractions

← "Flip over" the second fraction and change the division sign into a multiplication sign.

$\div 28$ is the same as $\times \frac{1}{28}$

$\div \frac{1}{3}$ is the same as $\times 3$

So $\div \frac{28}{3}$ is the same as $\times \frac{3}{28}$

Recurring decimals

A recurring decimal has a sequence of digits which repeat indefinitely, e.g. 0.333333…, 0.275275275…, 0.6781818181…

The recurring digits are shown like this:

$0.333333… = 0.\dot{3}$

$0.275275275… = 0.\dot{2}7\dot{5}$

$0.6781818181… = 0.67\dot{8}\dot{1}$

> Put a dot over the first digit and the last digit of the recurring part.

Comparing the sizes of decimals

You can write $57.8 = 50 + 7 + \dfrac{8}{10}$ and $57.812 = 50 + 7 + \dfrac{8}{10} + \dfrac{1}{100} + \dfrac{2}{1000}$

It is clear from this that 57.812 is larger than 57.8.

To compare the sizes of two decimals.

Compare the digits in the first decimal place.

0.5236 is larger than 0.4999

since the 5 is larger than the 4.

If the digits in the first decimal place are equal then compare the second decimal places.

0.682 is larger than 0.679

since 8 is larger than 7.

Continue in this way comparing digits.

When comparing 0.987 with 0.98 it is easier if you write 0.98 as 0.980.

0.987 is larger than 0.980

since 7 is greater than 0.

Example

Place these numbers in ascending order:

$\dfrac{34}{50}$ $\quad$ $\dfrac{2}{3}$ $\quad$ 0.66 $\quad$ 67% $\quad$ $\dfrac{13}{20}$

Write them all as decimal fractions.

$\dfrac{34}{50} = 0.68$ $\quad$ $\dfrac{2}{3} = 0.\dot{6}$ $\quad$ 0.66 $\quad$ 67% = 0.67 $\quad$ $\dfrac{13}{20} = 0.65$

So in ascending order they are:

$\dfrac{13}{20}$ $\quad$ 0.66 $\quad$ $\dfrac{2}{3}$ $\quad$ 67% $\quad$ $\dfrac{34}{50}$

Exam question
CIE 0580 June '06 Paper 1 Q2

0.09 $\quad$ 90% $\quad$ $\dfrac{9}{1000}$ $\quad$ 9% $\quad$ 0.9 $\quad$ $\dfrac{9}{100}$ $\quad$ 900%

Write down the three numbers from the list above which have the same value.

Write all the numbers as decimal fractions.

0.09 $\quad$ 90% = 0.9 $\quad$ $\dfrac{9}{1000} = 0.009$ $\quad$ 9% = 0.09 $\quad$ 0.9 $\quad$ $\dfrac{9}{100} = 0.09$ $\quad$ 900% = 9

The three equal numbers are 0.09, 9% and $\dfrac{9}{100}$.

Notation for comparing the sizes of numbers

The symbol ">" means greater than. So $x > 5$ means that x is greater than 5.

The symbol "<" means less than. So $x < 3$ means that x is less than 3.

The symbol "⩾" means greater than or equal to. So $x ⩾ 6$ means that x is greater than or equal to 6.

The symbol "⩽" means less than or equal to. So $x ⩽ -2$ means that x is less than or equal to -2.

Exam question
CIE 0580 November '05 Paper 1 Q14

Choose one of the symbols: $=$, $<$ or $>$, to complete each of the following statements.

When $x = 6$ and $y = -7$, then

(a) $x \ldots y$ (b) $x^2 \ldots y^2$ (c) $y - x \ldots x - y$

(a) $6 > -7$ so $x > y$
(b) $x^2 = 6^2 = 36,$ $y^2 = (-7)^2 = 49$ and $36 < 49$ so $x^2 < y^2$
(c) $y - x = -7 - 6 = -13,$ $x - y = 6 - -7 = 13$ and $-13 < 13$
 so $y - x < x - y$

Questions

1. A dowelling rod has length 150 cm. It is cut into pieces of length $1\frac{1}{4}$ cm. How many such pieces can be cut from the original rod?

2. A bottle of orange juice holds $2\frac{1}{2}$ litres of water. A glass holds $\frac{1}{8}$ litre. How many glasses can be filled from one bottle of orange juice?

3. (a) Express 0.375 as a fraction.
   (b) Express $\frac{3}{25}$ as a decimal.

4. Calculate the following:
   (a) $3\frac{1}{2} \times 5\frac{1}{3}$
   (b) $7\frac{3}{4} + 6\frac{2}{5}$
   (c) $8\frac{5}{6} - 3\frac{3}{8}$
   (d) $4\frac{1}{5} \div 2\frac{3}{7}$

5. Write these numbers in ascending order

   $\frac{41}{50}$ 0.8 $\frac{21}{25}$ 81%   0.85

6. If $x = 9$ and $y = 11$ write the correct sign, $<$, $=$ or $>$, in these expressions.
   (a) $x \ldots y$
   (b) $y - x \ldots x - y$
   (c) $12x \ldots y^2$

7. 0.037   37%   0.307 $\frac{3}{10}$ $\frac{3}{100}$ 3.7%

   From the numbers listed above write down
   (a) the smallest number
   (b) the largest number
   (c) the two numbers which are equal

8. Convert the following recurring decimals to fractions
   (a) $0.\dot{2}$
   (b) $0.\dot{6}\dot{1}$

7 Standard form

The mass of the Earth is about 5 974 200 000 000 000 000 000 000 kg, a very large number. The time taken for light to travel 1 km is about 0.000 003 335 56 seconds, a very small number. **Standard form** is useful when writing very large and very small numbers.

To write a number in standard form express it as a number between 1 and 10 multiplied by the appropriate power of 10.

$$\textcircled{a} \times 10^{n}$$

a is a number
between 1 and 10
$(1 \leqslant a < 10)$

n is a whole number,
positive for large numbers,
negative for small numbers.

So the mass of the Earth = 5.9742×10^{24} kg

| Some calculators display this as 5.9742E24 | Multiplying by 10^{24} moves the decimal place in 5.9742 by 24 places to the right. |

The time taken for light to travel 1 km = $3.335\,56 \times 10^{-6}$ seconds

| Some calculators display this as 3.33556E −6 | Multiplying by 10^{-6} moves the decimal place in 3.335 56 by 6 places to the left. |

Example
Write these numbers in standard form:

3 723 000   0.001 235   0.172   10.3   0.000 000 312   201

$3\,723\,000 = 3.723 \times 10^6$

$0.172 = 1.72 \times 10^{-1}$

$0.000\,000\,312 = 3.12 \times 10^{-7}$

$0.001\,235 = 1.235 \times 10^{-3}$

$10.3 = 1.03 \times 10^1$

$201 = 2.01 \times 10^2$

Example
Write 456 000 000 000 in standard form.

$456\,000\,000\,000 = 4.56 \times 100\,000\,000\,000 = 4.56 \times 10^{11}$

Example
Write 0.000 372 in standard form.

$0.000\,372 = 3.72 \times \dfrac{1}{10\,000} = 3.72 \times 10^{-4}$

M   Math ▲
3.72÷10000
          3.72×10⁻⁴

Exam question
CIE 0580 June '06 Paper 1 Q20

There are **565** sheets of paper in a book.
  (a) How many sheets of paper are there in **2000** of these books?
      Give your answer in standard form.
  (b) A pile of **565** sheets of paper is 25 mm high.
      Calculate the thickness of **1** sheet of paper.
      Give your answer in standard form.

(a) $2000 \times 565 = 1\,130\,000 = 1.13 \times 10^6$

(b) $25 \div 565 = 0.044\,247.... = 4.42 \times 10^{-2}$ mm (to 3 sf)

Questions

1. The distance from London to Beirut is approximately 3460 km. Express this number in standard form.

2. The distance from Auckland to Rio de Janeiro is approximately 12 260 km. Express this number in standard form.

3. The radius of the Earth is 6 378 100 m. Express this number in standard form.

4. The speed of light is given as 2.998×10^8 m s^{-1}. Express this as an ordinary number.

5. Express these numbers in decimal form (to 3 sf):
(a) 0.2^6 (b) 0.3^{15}
(c) 0.15^7 (d) 0.22^8

6. Give the values of these expressions in standard form (to 3 sf):
(a) 2^{30} (b) 3^{20} (c) $\left(\frac{1}{2}\right)^6$
(d) $\left(\frac{1}{3}\right)^3$ (e) $\sqrt{0.005}$ (f) $\left(\frac{1}{11}\right)^2$
(g) 5^{13} (h) $\sqrt{0.007}$ (i) $\left(\frac{3}{4}\right)^{10}$

7. Give your answers to these calculations in standard form (to 3 sf where necessary):
(a) $(3.4 \times 10^7) \times (4.2 \times 10^5)$
(b) $(2.9 \times 10^{15}) \times (2.1 \times 10^7)$
(c) $(7.2 \times 10^4) \times (1.3 \times 10^{-1})$
(d) $(3.91 \times 10^{-5}) \div (2.35 \times 10^{-7})$
(e) $(9.21 \times 10^7) \div (2.31 \times 10^{-5})$
(f) $(1.21 \times 10^{-5}) \div (1.24 \times 10^9)$

8. The population of the world at the end of 1995 was 5.2×10^9 people.
(a) The population was projected to grow by 4% in 1996. Calculate the projected population at the end of 1996, giving your answer in standard form (to 2 sf).
(b) In fact the population at the end of 1996 was 5.5×10^9. What was the percentage increase (to 2 sf) in the population over 1996?
(c) The projected population at the end of 2020 is 1.8×10^{10}. How many more people is this than at the end of 1995? (Give your answer in standard form to 2 sf.)

9. The density of water is 1×10^3 kg m^{-3}. Find the following (all in standard form):
(a) the mass of water (in kg) in a cuboid measuring 2 m by 3 m by 5 m
(b) the volume (in m^3) of water whose mass is 5×10^8 tonnes (one tonne is 1000 kg).
(c) the volume (in cm^3) of 1 m^3 of water.
(d) the mass (in g) of 1 m^3 of water.
(e) the density of water in g cm^{-3}.
(f) the mass of water (in g) in a cuboid measuring 6 cm by 3 cm by 10 cm.

10. The population of a certain country is 5.7×10^8 and its area is 7.21×10^4 km^2. Find the population density (people per m^2) of this country in standard form to 3 sf.

11. The diameter of the Earth is 1.3×10^7 m. Assuming that the Earth is a perfect sphere, find its circumference in km. Write the answer in standard form (to 2 sf).

12. The adult population of a country is 60 million. The average annual income per adult is $43 000. Find in standard form the total annual income from the adult population.

8 Estimation and limits of accuracy

Estimation

A website states that the distance between Cape Town and Cairo is 7234.15 km. However it is more realistic to give an estimation of this distance.

The distance can be stated to
(a) the nearest km
(b) the nearest 10 km
(c) the nearest 100 km.

(a) To the nearest km the distance is either 7234 km or 7235 km. It is clear that 7234.15 km is closer to 7234 km than to 7235 km. So the answer is 7234 km, to the nearest km.

(b) To the nearest 10 km the distance is either 7230 km or 7240 km. It is clear that 7234.15 km is closer to 7230 km than to 7240 km. So the distance is 7230 km, to the nearest 10 km.

(c) To the nearest 100 km the distance is either 7200 km or 7300 km. It is clear that 7234.15 km is closer to 7200 km than to 7300 km. So the distance is 7200 km, to the nearest 100 km.

Example

What is 9236.5 km to the nearest km?

9236.5 km is exactly halfway between 9236 km and 9237 km.
Use the rule that "5 or more is rounded up".
9236.5 km = 9237 km to the nearest km.

> When a number is exactly halfway between the two numbers the convention is that 5 is always **rounded up.**

When a number is rounded to 2 decimal places, there is no limit to how many digits it can have before the decimal point but **it must have exactly two digits after the decimal point**. Zeros are treated in the same way as any other number.

Example

Given that π = 3.141 592 653 589 793 238 46 ... find π correct to 2 dp.

π lies between 3.14 and 3.15, both of which are given to 2 dp.
3.14①592 653 589 793 238 46 rounds down to 3.14 since ① is less than 5.

So π = 3.14 (to 2 dp)

Rounding to 3 significant figures

Example

Write 17.298 correct to 3 significant figures.

17.298 lies between 17.2 and 17.3, both of which are given to 3 sf.

17.2⑨8 rounds up to 17.3 since ⑨ is "5 or more".

So 17.298 = 17.3 (to 3 sf).

Example
Write 18.047 correct to 3 significant figures.

18.047 lies between 18.0 and 18.1, both of which are given to 3 sf.

18.0④7 rounds down to 18.0 since ④ is less than five.

So 18.047 = 18.0 (to 3 sf).

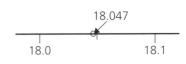

Small numbers
When rounding small numbers to 3 significant figures remember that the first significant digit is *the first non-zero digit* and that every digit after that is significant.

Example
Write 0.004 517 6 correct to 3 significant figures.

0.004 517 6 lies between 0.004 51 and 0.004 52, both of which are given to 3 sf.

0.004 51⑦6 rounds up to 0.004 52 since ⑦ is "5 or more".

So 0.004 517 6 = 0.004 52 (to 3 sf).

Be careful with numbers that have several zeros.

Large numbers
When rounding large numbers to 3 significant figures remember that the zeros at the end of the number are not (necessarily) significant.

Example
Write 2003 correct to 3 significant figures.

2003 lies between 2000 and 2010, both of which are given to 3 sf.

2003 rounds down to 2000 since 3 is less than 5.

So 2003 = 2000 (to 3 sf).

This can be confusing since you might be tempted to assume that 2000 only has one significant figure.

Example
Find an approximate answer to 19.79 − 2.31 × 3.15 by rounding each number to 1 sf.

The calculation becomes $20 - 2 \times 3 = 14$

Limits of accuracy

Upper and lower bounds
If the length of a rope is given as 5.3 m (to 2 sf) then you can calculate the upper and lower bounds of the length of the rope. That is you can calculate the longest and shortest possible values of the length of the rope.

To calculate the lower and upper bound think of the two numbers (to 2 sf) immediately above and below 5.3. These are 5.2 and 5.4.

The lower bound is halfway between 5.2 and 5.3. So 5.25 is the lower bound.
The upper bound is halfway between 5.3 and 5.4. So 5.35 is the upper bound.

If a length is given as 5.3 m (to 2sf) then it could be as short as 5.25 m and as long as 5.35 m.

You write 5.25 m ⩽ length < 5.35 m ◀—— NB You can say that 5.35 cm is the upper bound for 5.3 m even though 5.35 rounds to 5.4 m. This means that the number can be anything below 5.35m (so 5.34999999999....) **but never use recurring decimals as bounds.**

Example

The perimeter of a circle is given as 15 cm (to 2 sf).
Find the upper and lower bounds for the perimeter of the circle.

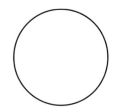

To calculate the lower and upper bound think of the two numbers (to 2 sf) immediately above and below 15. These are 14 and 16.

The lower bound is halfway between 14 and 15, that is 14.5.
The upper bound is halfway between 15 and 16, that is 15.5.

So 14.5 cm ⩽ perimeter < 15.5 cm

Exam question   CIE 0580 June '06 Paper 1 Q7

The population of a city is 350 000 correct to the nearest ten thousand. Complete the statement about the limits of the population.

$$\_\_ \leqslant \text{population} < \_\_$$

The numbers (correct to the nearest ten thousand) either side of 350 000 are 340 000 and 360 000.
The lower bound is halfway between 340 000 are 350 000, that is 345 000.
The upper bound is halfway between 350 000 are 360 000, that is 355 000.

So 345 000 ⩽ population < 355 000

Example

Joshua reads for 30 minutes each day (to the nearest 5 minutes). The total time he reads in April (30 days) is T minutes. Between what limits does T lie?

Find the two numbers (to the nearest 5 minutes) immediately above and below 30. These are 25 and 35.

The lower bound is halfway between 25 and 30, so 27.5.
The upper bound is halfway between 30 and 35, so 32.5.

So over the month the lower bound is 27.5 × 30 = 825 and the upper bound is 32.5 × 30 = 975.

So 825 min ⩽ T < 975 min

Combining measurements

Example

The dimensions of a rectangle are 12 cm and 8 cm to the nearest cm. Calculate, to 3 sf, the smallest possible area as a percentage of the largest possible area.

The lower and upper bounds for the 12 cm side are 11.5 cm and 12.5 cm respectively.

The lower and upper bounds for the 8 cm side are 7.5 cm and 8.5 cm respectively.

So the smallest possible area is 7.5 × 11.5 = 86.25 cm².

The largest possible area is 8.5 × 12.5 = 106.25 cm².

So the smallest possible area as a percentage of the largest possible area

$$= \frac{86.25}{106.25} \times 100\%$$

$$= 81.2\% \text{ (to 3 sf)}.$$

Extended

Extended

Example

The radius of a circle is given as 10 cm (to 2 sf). Find the minimum and maximum possible area of this circle.

> Be careful when dealing with multiples of 10. There is not the same symmetry as with other numbers

The two numbers (to 2 sf) immediately above and below 10 are 9.9 and 11.

The lower bound is halfway between 9.9 and 10, so 9.95.
The upper bound is halfway between 10 and 11, so 10.5.

Minimum possible area $= \pi \times 9.95^2 = 311$ cm^2 (to 3 sf).
Maximum possible area $= \pi \times 11^2 = 380$ cm^2 (to 3 sf).

Questions

1. (a) Estimate the values of these expressions by rounding all the numbers to 1 sf.

(i) $\dfrac{4.1 + 3.9 \times 2.1}{3.2}$ (ii) $\dfrac{9.1 \times 8.1 + 3.8 \times 7.2}{10.1}$

(iii) $\dfrac{14.1 + 6.9 \times 8.3}{8.9 - 2.1}$ (iv) $\dfrac{10.1^2 + 2.1 \times 20.7}{23.1 - 3.2}$

(b) Calculate the values of the above expressions, giving your answers to 3 sf.

2. (a) Find an estimate of the area of a circle of radius 9.97 cm.

(b) Calculate (to 3 sf) the area of a circle of radius 9.97 cm.

3. (a) Without using your calculator, and showing all you working, estimate (to 1 sf) the answer to this calculation:

$$\dfrac{2104.3 - (9.81)^2}{0.096}$$

(b) Using your calculator, find the answer to the calculation in part (a) to 3 sf.

4. Mount Kenya is 17 060 ft high, correct to the nearest twenty feet. Find the smallest possible height of Mount Kenya.

5. Write down the upper and lower bounds for each of these numbers:

(a) $w = 73.43$ (to 2 dp)
(b) $x = 7320$ (to 3 sf)
(c) $y = 7320$ (to 4 sf)
(d) $z = 147.037$ (to 3 dp)
(e) $a = 100$ (to 3 sf)
(f) $b = 100$ (to 1 sf)

6. The distance between Nairobi and Dar es Salaam is 671 km. Find this distance:

(a) to the nearest 10 km
(b) to the nearest 20 km
(c) to the nearest 50 km

7. The population of Nairobi in 2007 was estimated at 2 940 000 correct to the nearest ten thousand. Find the upper and lower bounds for the population.

Extended

8. A man runs a 100 m race and his time is measured as 10.3 s. If the track is accurate to the nearest metre and his time is accurate to the nearest 0.1 s then find the upper and lower bounds (to 1 dp) for his speed.

9. The area of a rugby field is 6950 m^2, correct to 3 sf. The length of the field is 95 m, correct to 2 sf.

(a) Find the upper and lower bounds for the area of the field.
(b) Find the upper and lower bounds for the length of the field.
(c) Use these to calculate the upper and lower bounds (to 3 sf) for the width of the field.

10. The formula for the distance s travelled by a body with initial speed u and constant acceleration a after a time t is given by $s = ut + \frac{1}{2}at^2$. Find the greatest and least possible values (to 3 sf) of s when $u = 6.1$, $a = 4.5$, $t = 13.6$ all correct to 1 dp.

11. Pythagoras' theorem states that $a^2 + b^2 = c^2$ where a, b and c are the three lengths of the sides of a right-angled triangle and c is the hypotenuse. If $a = 4.3$ cm and $c = 12.1$ cm, both correct to 1 dp, find the smallest and largest possible values for b (to 1 dp).

12. The formula $s = \dfrac{v^2 - u^2}{2a}$ is used to find the distance travelled by an object whose initial speed is u, whose final speed is v and whose acceleration is a. Find an inequality for s (to 2 sf) if, $v = 15$, $u = 11$ and $a = 2.3$, all correct to 2 sf.

9 Ratio, proportion and rate

Ratio

A school of 250 pupils has 150 boys and 100 girls.

The ratio of boys to girls is 150:100.

Simplest form

You can simplify a ratio by cancelling, for example, in its simplest form the ratio 150:100 = 3:2.

Cancel by the common factor 50

That means that for every 3 boys there are 2 girls.

Example

A sum of money is split between Arjun and Maya in the ratio 5:7. If Arjun gets $40 how much does Maya get?

> For every $5 Arjun gets, Maya gets $7.
> Arjun gets $40.
> $40 ÷ 5 = 8 so Arjun gets 8 lots of $5.
> So Maya gets 8 lots of $7 = $56

Example

Pulika, Shiva and Rafiki share sweets in the ratio 5:4:7. If there are 64 sweets in all then find how many does Rafiki gets?

> 5:4:7 means that there are 5 + 4 + 7 = 16 parts in all.
> Every part is $\frac{64}{16}$ = 4 sweets.
> Rafiki gets 7 parts which is 7 × 4 = 28 sweets.

Example

Peter buys 3 kg of carrots from a market and pays $4.50. How much would Lottie pay for 5 kg of carrots from the same market?

> 3 kg cost $4.50
> 1 kg costs $4.50 ÷ 3 = $1.50   5 kg costs $1.50 × 5 = $7.50
> Lottie pays $7.50.

Exchange rates

Example

Susan wanted to change some Canadian dollars into Kenyan shillings.
The exchange rate was 0.01592 Canadians dollars to the Kenyan shilling.
(a) How many Kenyan shillings did Susan get if she exchanged 500 Canadian dollars?
(b) At the end of her trip she exchanged 2000 Kenyan shillings back into Canadian dollars. How many Canadian dollars did she get?

> (a) Susan got one Kenyan shilling for every 0.01592 Canadian dollar.
>
> So she got $\frac{500}{0.01592}$ = 31 407 Kenyan shillings (to the nearest shilling)
>
> (b) For each Kenyan shilling she got 0.01592 Canadian dollars.
> So she got 2000 × 0.01592 = 31.84 Canadian dollars.

Direct proportion

As x increases y increases.

$y \propto x$ means that y is directly proportional to x.
$y \propto x$ can be rewritten as $y = kx$ where k is a constant that you can find.

For example, the number of apples, A, on a tree is proportional to the number of branches, b. If b doubles then A doubles.

In a similar way, $y \propto (x + 1)^2$ means that y is directly proportional to $(x + 1)^2$. This can be rewritten as $y = k(x + 1)^2$ where k is a constant.

Extended

Inverse proportion

$y \propto \dfrac{1}{x}$ means that y is inversely proportional to x. This can be rewritten as $y = \dfrac{k}{x}$ where k is a constant.

For example, the average speed of a runner, v, in a race is inversely proportional to the time, T, he takes to run the race. If T doubles then v halves.

In a similar way, $y \propto \dfrac{1}{\sqrt{x + 2}}$ means that y is inversely proportional to $\sqrt{x + 2}$. This can be rewritten as $y = \dfrac{k}{\sqrt{x + 2}}$ where k is a constant.

Solving problems involving proportion

In all cases the method is the same:

* Write the relation between x and y as an equation using k.
* Find k using a pair of values given in the question and replace k in the equation with this value.
* Use the equation to find other values of x and y.

Example

y is inversely proportional to x and $y = 24$ when $x = 5$. Find the value of
(a) y when $x = 2$
(b) x when $y = 30$.

* Write the relation between x and y as an equation using k.
$$y = \frac{k}{x}$$
* Find k using a pair of values given in the question.
When $x = 5$, $y = 24$ so $24 = \dfrac{k}{5}$ and so $k = 120$
Hence $y = \dfrac{120}{x}$
* Use the equation to find values of x and y.
(a) When $x = 2$, $y = \dfrac{120}{2} = 60$
(b) When $y = 30$, $30 = \dfrac{120}{x}$ and so $x = 4$

Example

Given that $y \propto \sqrt{x + 1}$ and that $y = 10$ when $x = 3$ find the value of
(a) y when $x = 15$
(b) x when $y = 30$.

* Write the relation between x and y as an equation using k.
$$y = k\sqrt{x + 1}$$
* Find k using a pair of values given in the question.
When $x = 3$, $y = 10$ so $10 = k\sqrt{3 + 1} = k\sqrt{4} = 2k$ and so $k = 5$
Hence $y = 5\sqrt{x + 1}$
* Use the equation to find values of x and y.
(a) When $x = 15$, $y = 5\sqrt{15 + 1} = 5\sqrt{16} = 20$
(b) When $y = 30$, $30 = 5\sqrt{x + 1}$
So $\sqrt{x + 1} = 6$, giving $x + 1 = 36$. Hence $x = 35$.

Exam question   CIE 0580 June '06 Paper 4 Q5

The length, y, of a solid is inversely proportional to the square of its height, x.
(a) Write down a general equation for x and y.
Show that when $x = 5$ and $y = 4.8$ the equation becomes $x^2y = 120$.
(b) Find y when $x = 2$.
(c) Find x when $y = 10$.
(d) Find x when $y = x$.
(e) Describe exactly what happens to y when x is doubled.

(Continued)

Extended

Exam question (Continued)

(f) Describe exactly what happens to x when y is decreased by 36%.

(g) Make x the subject of the formula $x^2y = 120$.

(a)
$$y = \frac{k}{x^2}$$

Replacing x with 5 and y with 4.8 gives $4.8 = \frac{k}{5^2}$ and so $k = 5^2 \times 4.8 = 120$

So $y = \frac{120}{x^2}$ which can be rewritten as $x^2y = 120$

(b) When $x = 2$, $2^2 \times y = 120$ and so $y = 30$.

(c) When $y = 10$, $x^2 \times 10 = 120$ and so $x^2 = 12$.

This gives $x = 3.46$ (to 3 sf)

(d) When $y = x$, replacing y with x gives $x^2 \times x = 120$. Hence $x^3 = 120$ and so
$x = 4.93$ (to 3 sf)

(e) When x is doubled y reduces by a factor of 4.

(f) When y is decreased by a factor of 36% y is multiplied by 0.64.

So x is multiplied by a factor of $\sqrt{\frac{1}{0.64}} = 1.25$. Hence x has increased by 25%.

(g) $x^2y = 120$

$$x^2 = \frac{120}{y}$$

$$x = \sqrt{\frac{120}{y}}$$

> $y - 36\%$ of y
> $= 64\%$ of y

Questions

1. A Bureau de Change offers $1.568 per £ sterling but charges a commission fee of £3. How many dollars (to the nearest cent) does Joe get for £75?

2. Anatole, Brij and Christophe receive $560 from their great aunt to be divided in the ratio Anatole : Brij : Christophe $= 3 : 5 : 6$
(a) Calculate how much each receives.
(b) Christophe puts all his share into a venture with Dimitri. If Dimitri adds to his share and puts in $300 altogether then find the ratio of Christophe's investment to Dimitri's investment.

3. If £1 $=$ €1.27 then find
(a) the cost (to the nearest £) of a holiday house which costs €450 per week
(b) how much (in €) a British holidaymaker would get for £300 at the foreign exchange.

4. When David's car was repaired, the charge for labour was $200. This was $\frac{4}{7}$ of the total bill. What was the total bill?

5. Mr Smith wants to turn 600 euros into Chinese yuan. The bank offers him a rate of 1 euro for 8.37 yuan.
(a) How many yuan does he get?
(b) At the end of his holiday Mr Smith has 100 Chinese yuan. If he changes his yuan back into euros at the same rate of exchange, how many euros does he get?

Extended

6. The distance, s, travelled by an object is directly proportional to the square of the time, t, for which it has been travelling. When $t = 5$, $s = 75$.
(a) Evaluate k, the constant of proportionality and write down an equation for s in terms of t.
(b) Find the value of s when $t = 7$.
(c) Find t when $s = 363$.
(d) Describe what happens when t is doubled

7. The mass, m, of an object is directly proportional to the cube of its side length, l. The mass of a cube with side length 3 cm is found to be 216 g.
(a) Calculate the constant of proportionality and write down an equation for m in terms of l.
(b) Find the mass of an object with side length 7 cm.
(c) Find the side length of an object which has mass 9261 g.
(d) Describe what has happened to l if m has increased by 33.1%.

8. The light intensity, I, is measured at a distance d away from a lamp. It is found that $I \propto \frac{1}{d^2}$. It is observed that $I = 180$ when $d = 7$.
(a) Find the constant of proportionality and write down an equation involving I and d.
(b) Find the value of I when $d = 2$.
(c) Find the value of d when $I = 45$.
(d) Describe what happens to d when I decreases by 75%.

10 Percentages

Percentages are used widely in the press, in politics, in business and in every area of life. For example in October 2008, inflation in Zimbabwe reached staggering new heights:

Hyperinflation in Zimbabwe
Zimbabwe's inflation rate surges to 231,000,000%

If a loaf of bread cost $2 on 9th October 2008 then what would it cost a week, a month or a year later?

When using percentages the total amount, whether it be the price of bread, the profits of a company, or the number of unemployed people, is split into 100 parts. Each part is one per cent of the total.

So 25% means 25 of these 100 parts, 17.5% means 17.5 of these 100 parts and so on.

Percentage calculations

Type 1

Example

What is 23% of $500?

$500 is 100%

1% is $\frac{500}{100}$ so 23% is $\frac{500}{100} \times 23 = \$115$

Quick alternative method:
$500 \times 0.23 = \$115$

Example

Find 12% of 1300 yards.

1% of 1300 is $\frac{1300}{100} = 13$ so 12% of 1300 is $13 \times 12 = 156$ yards.

Quick alternative method:
$1300 \times 0.12 = 156$ yards

Type 2

Example

If 17% of the total price is €1445 what is the total price?

€1445 is 17%.

1% is $\frac{1445}{17} = $ €85 so 100% is €85 $\times 100 = $ €8500

Quick alternative method:
$1445 \div 0.17 = $ €8500

Example

18% of the students at a school play tennis. If the school has 216 tennis players then how many students are there?

18% is 216, so 1% is $\frac{216}{18} = 12$ so 100% is $12 \times 100 = 1200$

Quick alternative method:
$216 \div 0.18 = 1200$

Type 3

Example

What percentage is 85 of 250?

Percentage $= \frac{\text{Amount}}{\text{Total}} \times 100\% = \frac{85}{250} \times 100\% = 34\%$

Example

A girl scored 75 out of 120 in a test. Find this as a percentage.

Percentage $= \frac{75}{120} \times 100\% = 62.5\%$

Percentage change

Example

In a sale the price of a shirt was reduced from £40 to £32. Find the percentage decrease.

In this case the original is £40 and the change in price is £8.

So percentage change $= \dfrac{\text{Change}}{\text{Original}} \times 100\% = \dfrac{8}{40} \times 100\% = 20\%$

All percentage change questions are type 3 questions. Always use the following....

Percentage change $= \dfrac{\text{Change}}{\text{Original}} \times 100\%$

Type 4

Example

A car worth €5000 loses 15% of its value in a year. What is it worth after one year?

1% of €5000 is $\dfrac{5000}{100} = €50$

15% of €5000 $= \dfrac{5000}{100} \times 15 = €50 \times 15 = €750$

The car is worth €5000 − €750 = €4250

Quick alternative method:
$5000 \times 0.85 = €4250$

Example

A football club's average attendance was 41 200. The following year the attendance rose by 4%. What was its new average attendance?

1% of 41 200 is $\dfrac{41200}{100} = 412$

4% is $412 \times 4 = 1648$

The average attendance increased by 1648 so the new average attendance was 42 848.

Quick alternative method:
$41200 \times 1.04 = 42\,848$

Example

The value of a house in 2007 was \$300 000. What was its value in 2008 after a fall of 8%?

1% of £300 000 is $\dfrac{300\,000}{100} = \$3000$ so 8% of £300 000 is $\$3000 \times 8 = \$24\,000$

So the value of the house in 2008 was \$300 000 − \$24 000 = \$276 000.

Quick alternative method:
$300\,000 \times 0.92 = \$276\,000$

Simple interest and compound interest

If you save money in a savings scheme (for example, with a bank, building society or the government) the initial amount you invest is called the **principal** and you receive interest on your money.

Similarly if you borrow money the lender will charge you interest.

Simple interest

When you invest money in a bank offering **simple interest** you only get interest on the original principal.

Example

Joseph invests \$500 at 4% per annum simple interest.
How much will he have at the end of 5 years?

Interest = 4% of \$500 $= \dfrac{4}{100} \times 500 = \$20$ per year

Total interest in 5 years = \$20 × 5 = \$100

Joseph will have \$500 + \$100 = \$600

"Per annum" (p.a.) means each year.

Example

Aruna invests €480 at 5% simple interest p.a.
What is her investment worth after
(a) 7 months   (b) 3 years?

(a)   5% of €480 = €24

A whole year's interest = €24

7 months' interest = €24 × $\frac{7}{12}$ = €14

After 7 months Aruna's investment will be worth €480 + €14 = €494

(b)   3 years' interest = 3 × €24 = €72

After 3 years Aruna's investment will be worth €480 + €72 = €552

Compound interest

When you invest money in a bank offering **compound interest** the interest you get each year is added to your principal and the next year's interest is paid on the increased amount in your account.

The compound interest formula is:

Value of investment = $P\left(1+\dfrac{r}{100}\right)^{n}$ where P is the amount invested, r is the percentage rate of interest and n is the number of years of compound interest.

Follow through these examples, checking the calculations as you go.

Example

Ali invests $200 at 3% compound interest. What amount will he have after 3 years?

3% of $200 = $6

$200 + $6 = $206 so Ali has $206 at the start of Year 2.

3% of $206 = $6.18

$206 + $6.18 = $212.18 so Ali has $212.18 at the start of Year 3.

3% of $212.18 = $6.37 to 2 dp

$212.18 + $6.37 = $218.55

Ali will have $218.55 after 3 years.

> Quick alternative method:
> $200 \times 1.03^3 = \$218.55$

> The principal increases by a factor of 1.03 each year so in three years it increases by a factor of 1.03^3.

Example

Rose borrows £800 at 7% compound interest for 2 years. How much does she owe at the end of two years?

7% of £800 = £56 so after one year Rose owes £856.

7% of £856 = £59.92

After two years Rose owes £856 + £59.92 = £915.92.

> Quick method
> Multiply by 1.07^2.

Example

A car loses 30% of its value each year. If it cost £18 000 then how much is it worth after 3 years?

£18 000 × 0.7^3 = £6174

The car is worth £6174 after 3 years.

> At the end of a year the car is worth 70% (0.7) of its value at the start of that year.

Extended

Reverse percentages

If you know the amount after a percentage increase or decrease then you can work out the original amount.

Example

The price of a skirt is reduced by 10% in a sale. If it cost $31.50 in the sale what was the original price of the skirt?

New price of skirt is $31.50.

This is 90% of the original price.

So 1% of the original price is $\frac{31.5}{90}$.

So the original price (i.e. 100%) was $\frac{31.5}{90} \times 100 = \$35$

> This question has **nothing** to do with finding 10% of $31.50.

> Quick method
> **Divide by 0.9.**
> $\$31.5 \div 0.9 = \$35$

Example

The price of a camera including VAT (value added tax) at 17.5% is $94. What was its price before VAT?

$94 is 117.5% of the price before VAT.

So 1% of the price before VAT was $\frac{94}{117.5}$.

So the original price (i.e. 100%) was $\frac{94}{117.5} \times 100 = \$80$

> You do **not** need to find 17.5% of $94.

> Quick method:
> $94 \div 1.175 = \$80$

The quick method

To go from the old price to the new price **multiply** by a factor.

To go from the new price to the old price **divide** by a factor.

Income tax

People who earn money often pay tax on their earnings. They usually receive a tax-free allowance.

Example

Juan earns $45 000 per year. He gets a tax free allowance of $8000 and pays tax at a rate of 25% on the next $20 000.
He then pays tax at a rate of 30% on his remaining income. How much tax does Juan pay?

$45\,000 - \$8000 = \$37\,000$
25% of $20\,000 = 20\,000 \div 4 = \$5000$
$37\,000 - \$20\,000 = \$17\,000$
30% of $17\,000 = 17\,000 \times 0.3 = \$5100$
Total tax $= \$5000 + \$5100 = \$10\,100$

Questions

1. A bank offers 5% compound interest on investments. A man invests £2000.
   (a) What is his investment worth after 2 years?
   (b) What is the total percentage increase?

2. A man buys plane tickets for himself, his wife and his four children. The adult fare is $172 and the child fare is 67% of the adult fare. Find the total cost of the journey.

Questions

3. An investment fund has increased in value by a total of 21% over the last two years.
(a) A man invested £1000 in the fund two years ago. What is it worth now?
(b) Calculate the yearly rate of interest assuming that it was:
   (i) compound interest   (ii) simple interest.

4. A bank offers 2% simple interest per year. A woman opens an account with a deposit of €750. She closes the account 11 months later. How much money does she withdraw?

5. In April a lawnmower cost £265. In the September sale it was only £225.25. What was the percentage discount?

6. A bleach bottle is labelled "900 ml for the price of 750 ml: x% extra free". The x is smudged and illegible. What is x?

7. Jack invests €80 in an account offering him 3.6% simple interest. He removes his money after 10 months. How much interest does he get?

8. The sale price of a garden table is £48 and it has a sign saying "Reduction of 20%". What was the price of the table before the sale?

9. A school claims that the pupils' average mark in an exam has increased by 15% over 5 years. Two boys are told that the average mark is now 85.1. George thinks that the average mark five years ago was 72.335 but James thinks it was 74. Who is right and how is the right answer obtained?

10. In a sale all items are reduced by 15%. A carpet now costs £15.30 per square metre. What was the price before the sale?

11. A document is photocopied so that the lengths of the copy are 70% of the original lengths. If the copy measures 12.6 cm by 17.5 cm what are the dimensions of the original document?

12. The attendance at a football match one week increased by $\frac{2}{3}$ from the previous week. If the new attendance was 45 000 what was the attendance the week before?

13. A boy's height increased by $\frac{1}{5}$ over a year. If his height is now 1.68 m what was his height a year ago?

14. The number of pupils at a school in 2006 was 85% of the number at the school in 2005. In 2006 the number of pupils was 1020. How many pupils were there in 2005?

15. Find the original price of a car which was sold for $1200 at a loss of 4%.

16. Find the original price of an antique which was sold at £545 at a profit of 9%.

17. The profit of a company in 2004 was £1 500 000. In 2005 the profit was 25% higher than it was in 2004 but in 2006 the profit fell by 40%.
(a) Show that the profit in 2005 was £1 875 000.
(b) What was the profit in 2006?

18. Julienne earns $73 000 per year. She gets a tax-free allowance of $7000 and then pays tax at a rate of 20% on the next $50 000. The tax rate on any additional income is then 40%. How much tax does Julienne pay overall?

11 Time and speed

Time problems

Example

A flight departed at 1514 and arrived at 1842. How long was the flight?

Three hours on from 1514 is 1814.

1842 is another 28 minutes on from that.

So the flight took 3 h 28 min.

Example

A girl arrived at a rehearsal at 1935 and left at 2129. For how long was she at the rehearsal?

One hour on from 1935 is 2035.

2035 to 2100 is another 25 minutes. 2100 to 2129 is a further 29 minutes. 25 + 29 = 54

So she was at the rehearsal for 1 hour 54 minutes.

Example

A plane leaves Shanghai at 1055 local time and arrives at London the same day at 1550 local time. The website says that the flight takes 12 h 55 min. How many hours is the time in London behind the time in Shanghai?

12 hours on from 1055 is 2255 and 55 min on from 2255 is 2350.

So the plane arrives at 2350 (Shanghai time). This is 1550 London time. So London is 8 hours behind Shanghai.

Example

Derek wanted to get from Twickenham to Wembley. A website gave him the information shown in the table.

(a) How long did the journey take in total?

(b) At which station did Derek wait for 8 minutes?

(a) He departed at 1158 and arrived at 1302. One hour would bring him to 1258 so there is another 4 minutes. So the journey took 1 h 4 min.

(b) There is an 8 minute gap between 1203 and 1211. So he waited for 8 minutes at Richmond Rail Station.

Depart Twickenham Rail Station	1158
Arrive Richmond Rail Station	1203
Depart Richmond Rail Station	1211
Arrive Willesden Junction Underground Station	1230
Depart Willesden Junction Underground Station	1235
Arrive Wembley Central Station	1242
Depart Wembley Central Station	1248
Arrive Wembley Stadium	1302

Time, distance and speed

Average speed

$$\text{average speed} = \frac{\text{total distance travelled}}{\text{total time taken}}$$

Be careful with units.

Example

A car travels 189 km at an average speed of 60 km/h, How long does the journey take?

Using $T = \frac{D}{S}$, $\quad T = \frac{189}{60} = 3.15$

The journey takes 3 h 9 min.

> 3.15 does not mean 3 h 15 min. It means 3 h and $0.15 \times 60 = 9$ min

To find the journey time given the start and end times:
- Calculate how many complete hours the journey has taken.
- Calculate the minutes.
- Combine the hours and minutes.

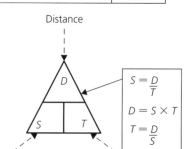

$S = \frac{D}{T}$

$D = S \times T$

$T = \frac{D}{S}$

Extended

Exam question

CIE 0580 June '07 Paper 4 Q1 b (ii)

A plane flies the 1580 km from Cairo to Khartoum.
It departs from Cairo at 1155 and arrives in Khartoum at 1403.
Calculate the average speed of the plane, in kilometres per hour.

1155 to 1355 is 2 hours. 1355 to 1403 is 8 minutes.

So the journey took 2 h 8 min.

2 h 8 min = $2\frac{8}{60}$ h = 2.1333...h ◄──── You must change the minutes to a decimal part of one hour.

The distance travelled is 1580 km.

Average speed = $\frac{1580}{2.13333...}$ = 740 km h^{-1} (to 3 sf)

24 hour clock

At midday a digital clock goes from 1159:59 to 1200:00 but at midnight the clock goes from 2359:59 to 0000:00 (not 2400:00).

7 hours on from 1900 is "2600", then subtract 24 to give 0200.

9 hours 45 minutes on from 2030 is "3015" then subtract 24 to give 0615.

Example

Lydia went to sleep at 2015 on Thursday and woke up at 0655 on Friday. For how long was she asleep?

0655 can be treated as "3055" (0655 + 2400 = 3055)

2015 to "3015" is 10 hours.

"3015" to "3055" is a further 40 minutes.

So Lydia was asleep for 10 hours 40 minutes.

Example

Mr Singh looks at his watch as the plane departs from Mumbai to Singapore and sees that it is 2050. If the journey lasts 8 h 30 min what time will his watch show when the plane arrives at Singapore?

8 hours on from 2050 is "2850". 8 hours 30 min on from 2050 is "2920". Subtract 24 to give 0520.

His watch will show 0520.

Other rates

Example

A 90 litre tank is filled full of water in 2 minutes and 15 seconds. What is the rate of flow (in litres per minute) of the water into the tank?

90 litres in 2.25 minutes = 90 ÷ 2.25 = 40 litres per minute

Example

An industrial heater uses energy at a rate of 30 kilowatts per hour. How many kilowatts of energy does it use in 24 hours?

24 hours at 20 kw/h = 24 × 30 = 720 kilowatts

Questions

1. A coach leaves London at 0655 and arrives in Glasgow at 1612, a distance of 667 km. Find the average speed in kilometres per hour.

2. A plane travels from Windhoek to Johannesburg in 1 h 45 min. If the distance is 1190 km find the average speed.

3. A plane leaves Nairobi airport at 2330 and arrives in London the next day at 0520. The time in Nairobi is 3 hours ahead of the time in London.
(a) How long does the flight take?
The return flight leaves London at 1005 and arrives in Nairobi at 2135.
(b) How long does the return flight take?
(c) Calculate how much longer the outward journey is than the return journey.
The distance between Nairobi and London is 6813 km.
(d) Find the average speeds of the plane on the outward and return journeys, in km h^{-1}.

4. A flight from Singapore to London leaves at 0130 local time and arrives the same day at 0555 local time. The airline website says that journey lasts for 12 h 25 min.
(a) How many hours ahead of London is Singapore?
(b) A traveller arriving at Singapore rings home when the time in Singapore is 0700. What is the time in London when he rings?
The airline website says that the exchange rate is such that the return trip costs 1780 Singaporean dollars, which is €913.80.
(c) At this exchange rate how much would a return trip of 2130 Singaporean dollars cost in euros?

5. A bucket is filled with water at a rate of 0.04 litres per second. If it takes 9 minutes to fill the bucket, what is the capacity of the bucket?

Example

The graph below shows the value of the Nigerian naira against the Kenyan shilling.

Use the graph to find

(a) how many Kenyan shillings you would get for 50 Nigerian naira

(b) how many Nigerian naira you would get for 60 Kenyan shillings.

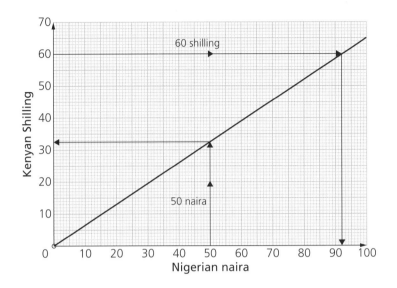

(a) Draw a vertical line up from 50 naira to the graph and then a horizontal line across to the vertical axis: 50 naira is about 33 shillings.

(b) Draw a horizontal line across from 60 shillings to the graph and then a vertical line down to the horizontal axis: 60 shillings is about 92 naira.

Example

The graph shows the amount that a shop charges for hiring a bike for up to 8 hours in a day.

There is an initial charge and then an hourly charge.

(a) What is the initial charge?

(b) What is the hourly charge?

(c) How much would it cost to hire a bike for 3 hours?

(d) How many hours' hire would cost $28?

(a) The initial charge is the cost when the time is zero.
   This is $10.

(b) From the graph you can see that 1 hour costs $13.
   So the hourly charge is $3.

(c) Reading off from graph gives $19.

(d) Reading off from graph gives 6 hours.

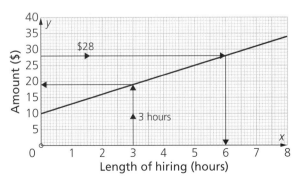

Extended

Distance-time graphs

> The gradient on a distance-time graph represents speed.

Exam question
CIE 0580 June '08 Paper 1 Q22

The diagram shows the graph of Rachel's journey on a motorway.
Starting at *A*, she drove 24 kilometres to *B* at a constant speed.
Between *B* and *C* she had to drive slowly through road works.
At *C* she drove a further distance to *D* at her original speed.

(a) For how many minutes did she drive through the road works?

(b) At what speed did she drive through the road works?
Give your answer in:
(i) kilometres/minute
(ii) kilometres/hour

(c) What is the total distance from *A* to *D*?

(a) She came to road works after 10 minutes and left them after
22 minutes. So she spent 12 minutes in the road works.

(b) (i) In 12 minutes her distance increased from 24 km to 34 km.
So the road works were 10 km long.
$$\text{Speed} = \frac{10}{12} = 0.833 \text{ km min}^{-1} \text{ (to 3 sf)}$$
(ii) $0.833 \ldots$ km min^{-1} = $0.833 \ldots \times 60$ km h^{-1} = 50 km h^{-1}

(c) Between *A* and *B* she travelled 24 km in 10 min.
Between *C* and *D* she travelled 12 km in 5 min (since she was travelling at
the same speed as from *A* to *B*).
Distance to *C* is 34 km so total distance from *A* to *D* is 46 km.

Extended

This graph shows the journey of a boy cycling. From the graph you can tell how the boy's
speed changes.

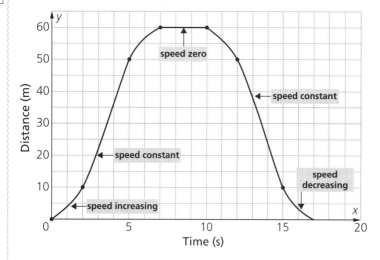

What happens to the speed…
Between 0 s and 2 s the boy is speeding up.
Between 2 s and 5 s the boy is travelling at a
constant speed.
Between 5 s and 7 s the boy is slowing down.
Between 7 s and 10 s the boy is stationary.
Between 10 s and 12 s the boy speeds up.
From 12 s to 15 s onwards the boy is travelling
at a constant speed.
From 15 s to 17 s the boy is slowing down.

Speed-time graphs

> Gradient on a speed-time graph represents acceleration.
> Area under a speed-time graph represents distance travelled.

This graph shows the speed of a toy car. From the graph you can tell how the car's speed
changes.

Extended

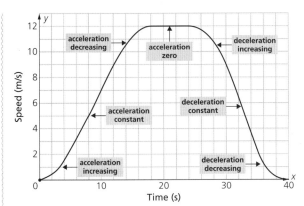

What happens to the speed

Between 0 s and 17 s the car is speeding up to reach a top speed of $12\,\text{m s}^{-1}$.

Between 17 s and 25 s the car has a constant speed of $12\,\text{m s}^{-1}$.

From 25 s onwards the car slows down (decelerates) to come to rest.

What happens to the acceleration

Between 0 s and 2 s the acceleration is increasing.

Between 2 s and 12 s the acceleration is constant.

Between 12 s and 17 s the acceleration is decreasing.

Between 17 s and 25 s the acceleration is zero

Between 25 s and 30 s the deceleration is increasing.

From 30 s to 35 s the deceleration is constant.

From 35 s the deceleration is decreasing.

Exam question

CIE 0580 June '06 Paper 4 Q1

1 (a) A train completed a journey of 850 kilometres with an average speed of 80 kilometres per hour. Calculate, giving exact answers, the time taken for this journey in

   (i) hours

   (ii) hours, minutes and seconds.

(b) Another train took 10 hours 48 minutes to complete the same 850 km journey.

   (i) It departed at 19 20. At what time, on the next day, did this train complete the journey?

   (ii) Calculate the average speed, in kilometres per hour, for the journey.

(c)

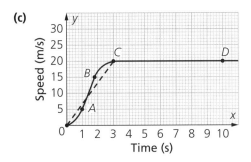

The *solid line OABCD* on the grid shows the first 10 seconds of a car journey.

   (i) Describe briefly what happens to the *speed* of the car between *B* and *C*.

   (ii) Describe briefly what happens to the *acceleration* of the car between *B* and *C*.

   (iii) Calculate the acceleration between *A* and *B*.

   (iv) Using the *broken* straight line *OC*, estimate the total distance travelled by the car in the whole 10 seconds.

   (v) Explain briefly why, in this case, using the broken line makes the answer to part **(iv)** a good estimate of the distance travelled.

   (vi) Calculate the average speed of the car during the 10 seconds.
Give your answer in kilometres per hour.

(a) (i) $T = \dfrac{D}{S} = \dfrac{850}{80} = 10.625$ hours

   (ii) 0.625 h is $0.625 \times 6 = 37.5$ min = 37 min and 30 seconds
So the journey time is 10 h 37 min and 30 sec.

(b) (i) 10 hours on from 1920 is '2920' which is 0520 the next day. Another 48 minutes brings it to 0608.

   (ii) 48 min is $\dfrac{48}{60} = 0.8$ h
So 10 h 48 min is 10.8 h.
Average speed = $850 \div 10.8 = 78.7\ \text{km h}^{-1}$ (to 3 sf)

(c) (i) The speed of the car increases from $15\ \text{m s}^{-1}$ to $20\ \text{m s}^{-1}$.

   (ii) Between *B* and *C* the curve is getting less steep so the acceleration is decreasing.

   (iii) *A* is the point (1, 5) and *B* is the point (1.8, 15)
Gradient = $\dfrac{15 - 5}{1.8 - 1} = \dfrac{10}{0.8} = 12.5\ \text{m s}^{-2}$

   (iv) Distance is area under graph:
Total area is $30 + 140 = 170$
Total distance travelled = 170 m

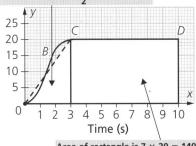

Area of triangle is $\frac{1}{2} \times 3 \times 20 = 30$

Area of rectangle is $7 \times 20 = 140$

   (v) The area of the graph below the dotted line about the same as the area of the graph above the dotted line.

   (vi) The car travelled 170 m in 10 s.
Average speed $= \dfrac{170}{10} = 17\ \text{m s}^{-1} = 17 \times 60 \times 60\ \text{m h}^{-1} = 61\,200\ \text{m h}^{-1} = 61.2\ \text{km h}^{-1}$

Extended

Questions

1. The graph below shows the amount an electrician charges for up to five hours' work.
   (a) What does the electrician charge for being called out?
   (b) How much does he charge for 2 hours' work?
   (c) If he charged Mr Bali $210 then how many hours work did he do?
   (d) A second electrician had a call out fee of $60 and an hourly fee of $35. For how many hours work would the two electricians charge the same amount?

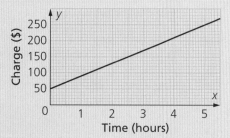

2. A coach was hired to take a school team to a football game. The graph shows the distance travelled from the school.
   (a) How far did the coach travel before stopping?
   (b) For how long did the coach stop?
   (c) How much further did the coach travel to the game?
   (d) How long did the coach wait at the game?
   (e) How long did the return journey take?
   (f) What was the average speed of the coach on the return journey?

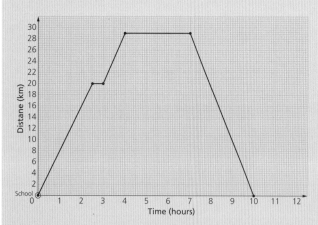

3. Hasnain drove to see a friend. The graph shows his journey to and from his friend's house and the time he spent with his friend.
   (a) How long it take for Hasnain to reach a constant speed?
   (b) What was happening to his speed in the first 5 minutes?

   (c) What was the constant speed in km h⁻¹?
   (d) How long did Hasnain spend at his friend's house?
   (e) What was his constant speed for the last 11 minutes of his journey?

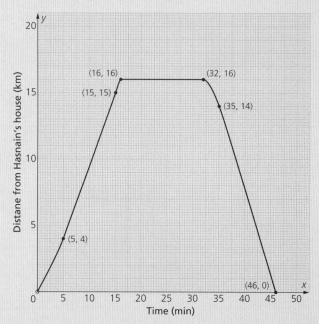

4. Awais was on a fast road and the graph shows his journey.
   (a) How long did it take Awais to reach a constant speed?
   (b) How far did he travel at this constant speed?
   (c) What was happening to his acceleration in the first minute?
   (d) By using the dotted lines for the first minute and the last 30 seconds estimate how far Awais travelled.
   (e) Is this an under-estimate or an over-estimate of the distance that Awais travelled? Give a reason for your answer.

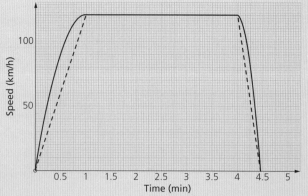

13 Graphs of functions

Example
The table gives the values of *x* and *y* for the function *y* = 3*x* + 2.

x	−1	0	1	2	3	4	5
y		2	5	8	11		

(a) Fill in the missing values of y.
(b) Sketch the graph of *y* = 3*x* + 2.
(c) Use your graph to solve the equation, 3*x* + 2 = 10.

(a) To find the *y*-value when *x* = −1 substitute −1 for *x* into 3*x* + 2.

 not

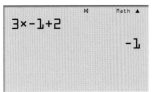

Repeating this for *x* = 4 and *x* = 5 gives:

x	−1	0	1	2	3	4	5
y	−1	2	5	8	11	14	17

(b) Mark the points on the graph, that is (−1, −1), (0, 2) etc.

Join the points using a straight line.

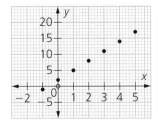

> REMEMBER
> *x*-axis is **horizontal**
> *y*-axis is **vertical**
>
> (Alphabetical order in both): *x, y, h, v.*

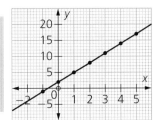

(c) The solution to 3*x* + 2 = 10 is the *x*-coordinate of the point on the graph where *y* = 3*x* + 2 meets *y* = 10

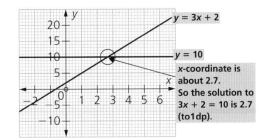

y = 3*x* + 2

y = 10

x-coordinate is about 2.7.
So the solution to 3*x* + 2 = 10 is 2.7 (to 1 dp).

Graphs of quadratic functions
The basic shape of the graph of $y = ax^2 + bx + c$ is shown in these diagrams.
(i) $a > 0$ (ii) $a < 0$

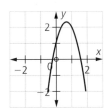

The turning point of the quadratic function can be anywhere and it is determined by the particular values of a, b and c.

Example

The table gives the values of x and y for the function $y = x^2 - 4x + 4$.

x	-1	0	1	2	3	4	5
y		4	1		1		9

(a) Fill in the missing values of y.
(b) Sketch the graph of $y = x^2 - 4x + 4$.
(c) Use the graph to solve $x^2 - 4x + 4 = 7$.

    (a) To find the value of y when $x = -1$ substitute -1 for x into $x^2 - 4x + 4$.

    Use brackets on the calculator, so type in $(-1)^2 - 4(-1) + 4$ to get 9.

    Repeating this for the values 2 and 4 gives:

x	-1	0	1	2	3	4	5
y	9	4	1	0	1	4	9

M   Math ▲

$(-1)^2 - 4 \times (-1) + 4$

9

    (b) Mark the points on the graph, that is $(-1, 9)$, $(0, 4)$ etc.

    Join the points using a smooth curve.

The solutions to $x^2 - 4x + 4 = 7$ are the x-coordinates of the points on the graph where $y = x^2 - 4x + 4$ meets $y = 7$.

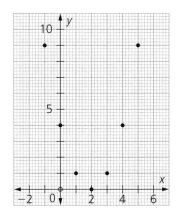
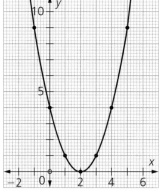
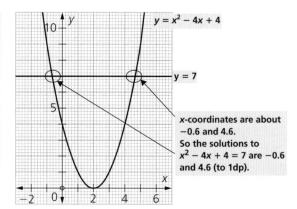

$y = x^2 - 4x + 4$

$y = 7$

x-coordinates are about -0.6 and 4.6.
So the solutions to $x^2 - 4x + 4 = 7$ are -0.6 and 4.6 (to 1dp).

Example

The table gives the values of x and y for the function $y = \dfrac{24}{x}$.

x	-4	-3	-2	-1	0	1	2	3	4
y	-6	-8			$-$		12	8	

(a) Fill in the missing values of y.

(b) Sketch the graph of $y = \dfrac{24}{x}$.

    (a) To find the value of y when $x = -2$ substitute -2 for x into $\dfrac{24}{x}$ to give $y = -12$.

    Repeating this for -1, 2 and 4 gives:

x	-4	-3	-2	-1	0	1	2	3	4
y	-6	-8	-12	-24	$-$	24	12	8	6

You cannot write a value for y when $x = 0$ since it is not possible to divide by zero.

(b) Mark the points on the graph, that is $(-4, -6)$, $(-3, -8)$ etc.

Join up the points using a smooth curve.

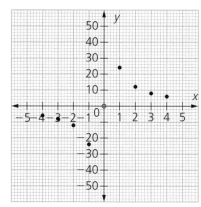

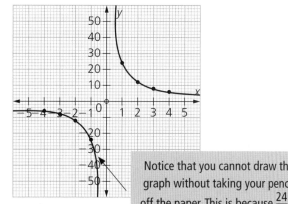

Notice that you cannot draw the graph without taking your pencil off the paper. This is because $\frac{24}{x}$ is undefined when $x = 0$.

Example

A curve has equation $y = f(x)$ where $f(x) = 4x - \dfrac{1}{x^2} + 2$, $x \neq 0$.

(a) The table shows some values of $f(x)$:

x	-3	-2.5	-2	-1.5	-1	-0.5	0.5	1	1.5	2	2.5	3
y	-10.1	a	-6.3	-4.4	b	-4	0	5	7.6	9.8	11.8	c

Find the values (to 1 dp) of a, b and c.

(b) Draw a sketch of $y = f(x)$.

(c) Estimate the gradient of the curve at the point where $x = 2$.

(a) The best way to fill in such a table is to use your calculator efficiently.
Some calculators have the table facility; a, b and c can be found easily using the table.

If not, then almost all calculators enable you to store values into the memory.

Store -2.5 in the memory X.

So $a = -8.2$ (to 1 dp)

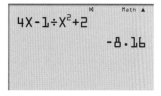

Now store -1 in the memory. On many calculators you can scroll up to $4X - 1/X^2 + 2$.

Press ⬜= to get -3. So $b = -3$

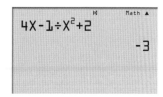

A similar method gives $c = 13.9$

(b) Plot the points and join them.

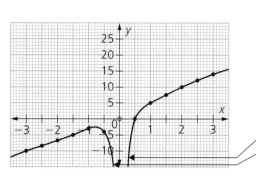

NB When a curve has a term such as $\frac{4}{x}$ or $\frac{5}{x^2}$ then it will either head almost vertically downwards or almost vertically upwards as x gets close to 0.

In this example the term is $-\dfrac{1}{x^2}$ so for small positive and small negative values of x, the term $-\dfrac{1}{x^2}$ becomes a very "large" negative value.

Extended

(c) To find the gradient at $x = 2$ draw a tangent at this point and calculate its gradient.

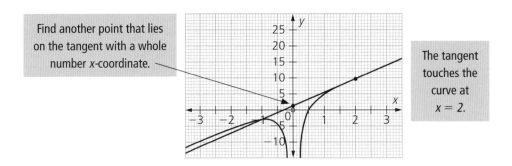

Find another point that lies on the tangent with a whole number x-coordinate.

The tangent touches the curve at $x = 2$.

So the tangent roughly goes through the point (0, 1) and also goes through (2, 9.8) (from the initial table).

Hence the gradient of the curve at the point where $x = 2$ is $\dfrac{9.8 - 1}{2 - 0} = \dfrac{8.8}{2} = 4.4$

So the gradient is approximately 4 at the point on the curve where $x = 2$.

Graph of $y = a^x$

When $a > 0$ the graph of $y - a^x$ has this basic shape:

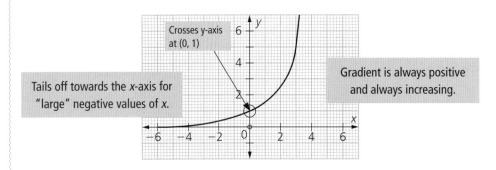

Crosses y-axis at (0, 1)

Tails off towards the x-axis for "large" negative values of x.

Gradient is always positive and always increasing.

Using graphs to solve equations

Example

The graphs of $y = x^3 - 4x^2 + 5$ and $y = 4 - 2x$ are shown in the diagram.

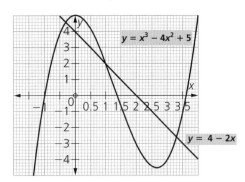

$y = x^3 - 4x^2 + 5$

$y = 4 - 2x$

(a) Use the graph to solve $x^3 - 4x^2 + 5 = 4 - 2x$.

(b) Find an integer value of k for which $x^3 - 4x^2 + 5 = k$ has three solutions.

(a) The solution to $x^3 - 4x^2 + 5 = 4 - 2x$ is the x-coordinate of the point (or points) of intersection of the two graphs.

From the diagram they intersect when $x = -0.3$, $x = 1$ and $x = 3.3$.

So the solutions to $x^3 - 4x^2 + 5 = 4 - 2x$ are $x = -0.3$, $x = 1$ and $x = 3.3$.

(b) The solution to $x^3 - 4x^2 + 5 = k$ is the x-coordinate of the point (or points) of intersection of the curve $y = x^3 - 4x^2 + 5$ and the horizontal line $y = k$.

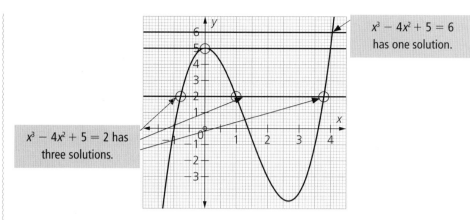

$x^3 - 4x^2 + 5 = 6$ has one solution.

$x^3 - 4x^2 + 5 = 2$ has three solutions.

If $-4 \leq k \leq 4$ then $x^3 - 4x^2 + 5 = k$ has three solutions.

Drawing a straight line to solve an equation

Example

The graph of $y = x^3 - 5x + 2$ is shown in the diagram. Draw a straight line on the graph to solve the equation $x^3 - 6x + 4 = 0$.

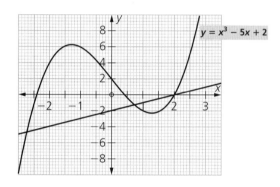

$y = x^3 - 5x + 2$

Step 1

Write down the equation you have to solve.   So $x^3 - 6x + 4 = 0$

Step 2

Write underneath this   So $x^3 - 5x + 2 = y$
the equation of the curve that has been drawn, with
corresponding terms aligned.

> Align the x^3-terms, the x-term and the constant terms.

Step 3

Work out what you have to do to the left-hand side
of the equation in Step 1 to get the equation in step 2.
Do the same to the right-hand side. So in this example

$$x^3 - 6x + 4 = 0$$
$$\begin{array}{cccc} +x & -2 & +x & -2 \end{array}$$
$$x^3 - 5x + 2 = x - 2$$

> Add $x - 2$ to both sides.

Step 4

Step 3 tells you that solving $x^3 - 6x + 4 = 0$,
is the same as solving $x^3 - 5x + 2 = x - 2$, so draw the graph of $y = x - 2$.
The solution is where $y = x - 2$ intersects $y = x^3 - 5x + 2$.

Reading off the x-coordinates of the points of intersection gives $x = -2.7, 0.7$ or 2.

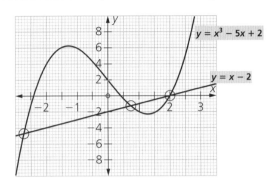

Questions

1. This table of values is for the graph $y = x^2 - 6x + 1$.

x	0	1	2	3	4	5	6
y			-7				

(a) Copy and complete the table.

(b) Draw a scale from 0 to 6 on the x-axis (2 cm per unit) and from −10 to 5 on the y-axis (1 cm per unit).

(c) Draw a sketch of the curve $y = x^2 - 6x + 1$.

(d) Use your graph to find the values of x (to 1 dp) when $y = 0$ and $y = -5$.

2. This table of values is for $y = x^2 - 2x - 20$.

x	-5	-4	-3	-2	-1	0	2	3
y	15	4	-5		-17		-20	-17

4	5	6	7
	-5	4	

(a) Copy and complete the table.

(b) Draw a scale from −5 to 7 on the x-axis (1 cm per unit) and from −30 to 40 on the y-axis (2 cm per 5 units). Draw a sketch of the curve $y = x^2 - 2x - 20$.

(c) Copy and complete the table of values for $y = \frac{24}{x}$.

x	-5	-4	-3	-2	-1	0	1
y	-4.8	-6.0			-24.0	–	24.0

2	3	4	5	6	7
12.0	8.0		4.8		3.4

(d) On the same diagram as part (b) draw the graph of $y = \frac{24}{x}$ for $-5 \leqslant x \leqslant 7$.

(e) Write down the x-coordinate of the two intersection points of the two graphs. These two x-values are the solution to an equation. Write down and simplify this equation.

3. The table of values is for the graph $y = x^2 - 2x - 4$.

x	-3	-2	-1	0	1	2	3	4	5
y								4	

(a) Copy and complete the table.

(b) Draw a scale from −3 to 5 on the x-axis (2 cm per unit) and from −8 to 12 on the y-axis (1 cm per unit).

(c) Draw a sketch of the curve $y = x^2 - 2x - 4$.

(d) Use your graph to solve (to 1 dp) the equation $x^2 - 2x - 4 = 0$.

(e) Use your graph again to solve (to 1 dp) the equation $x^2 - 2x - 4 = 5$.

(f) What is the smallest value of $x^2 - 2x - 4$ and which value of x achieves this smallest value?

4. The diagram shows a graph of $y = f(x)$

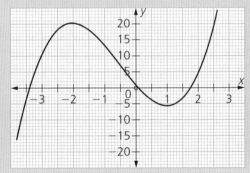

(a) Use the graph to find
   (i) f(1)   (ii) f(−1)

(b) Use the graph to solve
   (i) $f(x) = 5$ (ii) $f(x) = 10$

(c) k is an integer for which $f(x) = k$ has three different solutions. Use the graph to find an inequality for k.

(d) Write down an inequality for x for which the gradient of $y = f(x)$ has a positive gradient.

5. Draw the graph of $y = 2^x$ using x values from −1 to 5 (1 cm per unit) and a scale of 1 cm per 5 units on the y-axis. Find the approximate value of x when $y = 10$.

14 Straight line graphs

Equations of straight lines

The equation of any straight line can be written in the form

$$y = mx + c$$

m is the gradient and c is the y-intercept.

The gradient, m, is a measure of how steep the line is.

$$m = \frac{\text{change in } y}{\text{change in } x}$$

m is positive if the line slopes upwards from left to right.

m is negative if the line slopes downwards from left to right.

The intercept of a straight line is the y-coordinate of the point where the line crosses the y-axis.

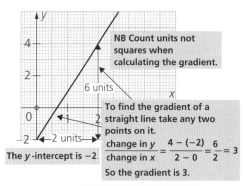

NB Count units not squares when calculating the gradient.

6 units

2 units

The y-intercept is −2.

To find the gradient of a straight line take any two points on it.

$\dfrac{\text{change in } y}{\text{change in } x} = \dfrac{4 - (-2)}{2 - 0} = \dfrac{6}{2} = 3$

So the gradient is 3.

So the equation of the line is $y = 3x - 2$.

Remember

Straight lines with positive gradients go uphill as they move from left to right, so they look like this :

Straight lines with Negative gradients go downhill as they move from left to right, so they look like this:

Negative

Drawing straight lines

Example
Draw the line $y = 5 + 2x$.

This line has a y-intercept of 5 and a gradient of 2.

Set up a table of three values:

x	0	2	3
y	5	9	11

Plot these three points and draw a line through them. →

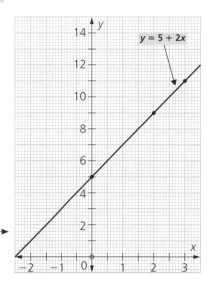

$y = 5 + 2x$

Example
Draw the line $y = 8 - \frac{2}{3}x$.

The line has a y-intercept of 8 and a gradient of $-\frac{2}{3}$.
Set up a table of values. Since the gradient is $-\frac{2}{3}$,
choose values of x that are multiples of 3.

x	0	3	9
y	8	6	2

Plot the points and draw the line.

Sometimes the equation is in a different form as in the next example.

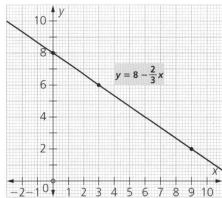

$y = 8 - \frac{2}{3}x$

Example
Draw the line $3x - 5y = 15$.

Method 1
Rearrange the equation to give $y = \frac{3}{5}x - 3$ and use the method shown above.

Method 2
(a) Put $y = 0$ in the equation:
$$3x = 15$$
$$x = 5$$
So (5, 0) is a point on the line.

(b) Put $x = 0$ in the equation:
$$-5y = 15$$
$$y = -3$$
So (0, −3) is a point on the line.

Plot and join the two points.

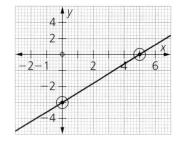

Finding the gradient and intercept of a straight line

- If the equation is in the form $y = mx + c$ the gradient and y-intercept can be seen immediately.
  For example, for the line $y = 6x - 7$ the gradient is 6 and the y-intercept is −7.
- If the equation is not in the form $y = mx + c$ the gradient and y-intercept cannot be seen immediately. Rewrite the equation to make y the subject.
  For example, to find the gradient and y-intercept of the line $9x + 2y = 7$, rewrite the equation as $y = -\frac{9}{2}x + \frac{7}{2}$. The gradient is $-\frac{9}{2}$ and the intercept is $\frac{7}{2}$.

Example
The equation of a straight line can be written in the form $5x + 4y - 12 = 0$.
(a) Rearrange the equation to make y the subject.
(b) Write down the gradient of the line.
(c) Find the coordinates of the point where the line crosses the y-axis.

(a) $5x + 4y - 12 = 0$
$$4y = 12 - 5x$$
$$y = 3 - \frac{5}{4}x$$
(b) The gradient of the line is $-\frac{5}{4}$.
(c) The y-intercept is 3 so the line crosses the y-axis at (0, 3).

Parallel lines

If two lines are parallel they have the same gradient. So $y = 3x + 1$ and $y = 3x - 5$ are parallel lines since they both have gradient 3.

Example
Find the line parallel to $y = 3x - 2$ which crosses the y-axis at the point (0, 5).

A line parallel to $y = 3x - 2$ has gradient 3.
A line passing through (0, 5) has y-intercept 5.
So the equation of the line is $y = 3x + 5$.

Finding the equation of a straight line

You can use one method of finding the equation of a line if you know the gradient of the line and a point through which it passes.

Example
Find the equation of the straight line with gradient 2 which passes through the point (3, 11).

The equation of a straight line is $y = mx + c$.

$m = 2$ so the equation is $y = 2x + c$.

The line passes through (3, 11) so
$$11 = 2 \times 3 + c$$
$$c = 5$$

Hence the equation is $y = 2x + 5$.

Put $x = 3$ and $y = 11$ in the equation
$$y = 2x + c$$

You can use another method of finding the equation of a line if you know two points through which the line passes.

Example

Find the equation of the straight line which passes through the points (2, 13) and (5, 28).

The gradient of the line is $\dfrac{\text{change in } y}{\text{change in } x} = \dfrac{28 - 13}{5 - 2} = \dfrac{15}{3} = 5$

So the equation of the line is $y = 5x + c$.

The line passes through (2, 13) so:

$13 = 5 \times 2 + c$

$c = 3$

Hence the equation is $y = 5x + 3$.

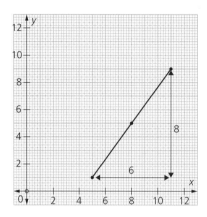

Example

Find the midpoint of the line joining the points (5, 1) and (11, 9). Find also the distance between these two points.

The midpoint is found by calculating the means of the x- and y- coordinates of the two points. So the midpoint of the line joining (5, 1) and (11, 9)

is $\left(\dfrac{5 + 11}{2}, \dfrac{1 + 9}{2}\right) = (8, 5)$

The distance between the points is calculated by using Pythagoras' theorem.

Distance $= \sqrt{(11 - 5)^2 + (9 - 1)^2} = \sqrt{6^2 + 8^2} = 10$

Perpendicular lines

If two lines are perpendicular, the product of their gradients is -1: $m_1 \times m_2 = -1$

Example

Find the equation of the straight line through (3, 1) that is perpendicular to the line $y = 0.5x + 1$.

Gradient of the perpendicular line: $-1 \div 0.5 = -2$

The equation of a straight line is $y = mx + c$ and $m = -2$ so $y = -2x + c$

The line passes through (3, 1) so

$1 = -2 \times 3 + c$

$c = 7$

Hence the equation is $y = -2x + 7$

Exam question
CIE 0580 November '06 Paper 2 Q21 b

In the diagram, the line AC has equation $2x + 3y = 17$ and the line AB has equation $4x - y = 6$.
The lines BC and AB intersect at $B(1, -2)$.
The lines AC and BC intersect at $C(4, 3)$.

Find the equation of the line BC.

The gradient of the line is $\dfrac{\text{change in } y}{\text{change in } x} = \dfrac{3 - (-2)}{4 - 1} = \dfrac{5}{3}$

So the equation of BC is $y = \dfrac{5}{3}x + c$.

Since the line goes through the point (4, 3)

$3 = \dfrac{5}{3}(4) + c$

Hence $c = -\dfrac{11}{3}$

The equation of BC is $y = \dfrac{5}{3}x - \dfrac{11}{3}$

or $3y = 5x - 11$

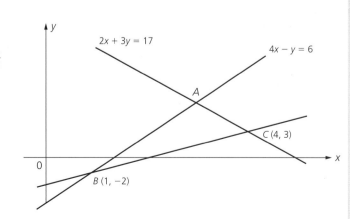

Extended

Questions

Extended

1. Find the gradient of the line $2y - 5x = 11$.

2. Find the equation of the line which passes through (4, 1) and is parallel to the line $y = 6x - 2$.

3. Two points A and B have coordinates (5, 7) and (−1, 3).
   (a) Find the midpoint of the line AB.
   (b) Find the length AB (to 3 sf)
   (c) Find the gradient of AB.
   (d) Find the equation of the line which passes through A and B.

Extended

4. Write down the coordinates of the points where the line $2y + 3x = 12$ crosses the x-axis and the y-axis.

5. Fill in the table for the line $y = \frac{3}{5}x - 2$.

x	0	5	10
y			

6. Find the equation of the straight line through (4, 2) that is perpendicular to the line $y = -2x + 3$.

15 Algebraic formulae

Using formulae

Example

A farmer pays $20 per bag of fertiliser, plus a fixed delivery fee of $30.

(a) Find the cost C, for n bags of fertiliser.

(b) How many bags can the farmer buy for $110?

(a) n bags at $20 per bag costs $20n$.

Delivery costs $30.

Total cost $C = 20n + 30$

(b) $110 = 20n + 30$ Subtract 30 from each side.

$80 = 20n$ Divide each side by 4

$n = 4$

The farmer can buy 4 bags for $110.

Example

p and q are related by the formula $p = 20q + 300$.

Find the value of p when $q = 25$.

Replace q with 25 in the formula:

$p = 20 \times 25 + 300$

$= 800$

```
20×25+300
                    800
```

Example

C and r are related by the formula $C = 20 - 0.5r$.

Find the value of C when $r = -6$.

Replace r with -6 in the formula:

$C = 20 - 0.5 \times (-6)$

$= 20 + 3$

$= 23$

```
20-0.5x-6
                    23
```

Example

If $D = \dfrac{(a - b)^2}{c^3}$ find the value of D when $a = 7$, $b = -2$ and $c = 3$.

$D = \dfrac{(7 - (-2))^2}{3^3}$

$= \dfrac{9^2}{3^3}$

$= 3$

```
(7-(-2))²÷3³
                    3
```

Rearranging formulae

To make x the subject of any formula use the following steps:

Step 1 Clear the fractions.

Step 2 Multiply out any brackets involving x.

Step 3 Put x-terms together alone on one side of the formula.

Step 4 Divide both sides by coefficient of x-term.

Example

Make x the subject of the formula $2x + 3b = c$.

Step 1 Clear the fractions.   No fractions

Step 2 Multiply out any brackets involving x.   No brackets to multiply out

Step 3 Put x-terms together on one side.

$2x = c - 3b$

Step 4 Divide by coefficient of x-term.

$x = \dfrac{c - 3b}{2}$

> Coefficient of x-term is 2.

Example

Make x the subject of the formula $\frac{ax + b}{x} = c$

Step 1 Clear the fractions.

$$ax + b = c \times x = cx$$

Step 2 Multiply out any brackets involving x.   No brackets to multiply out

Step 3 Put x-terms on one side.

$$cx - ax = b$$
$$x(c - a) = b$$

> When x appears twice factorise to give $x(c - a) = b$

Step 4 Divide by coefficient of x.

$$x = \frac{b}{c - a}$$

Example

Make x the subject of the formula $\frac{a}{x} + b = c$

Step 1 Clear the fractions.

$$a + bx = cx$$

Step 2 Multiply out any brackets involving x.   No brackets.

Step 3 Put x-terms on one side and write as $x(\ ) = \ldots$

$$a = cx - bx$$
$$a = x(c - b)$$

Step 4 Divide by coefficient of x.

$$x = \frac{a}{c - b}$$

If the equation involves x^2 then, first of all, make x^2 the subject and then take the square root of both sides to find x. Include the $\pm$ sign when taking square roots.

Example

Make x the subject of the formula $a = \frac{bx^2 + c}{d}$

Step 1 Clear the fractions.

$$ad = bx^2 + c$$

Step 2 Multiply out any brackets involving x^2.   No brackets.

Step 3 Put x^2-term on one side.

$$ad - c = bx^2$$

Step 4 Divide by coefficient of x^2.

$$x^2 = \frac{ad - c}{b}$$

Step 5 Take square roots.

$$x = \pm \sqrt{\frac{ad - c}{b}}$$

Questions

1. The acceleration of a body, moving with uniform acceleration, is given by the formula
$$a = \frac{v - u}{t}.$$
In this formula a is the uniform acceleration, u is the initial velocity and v is the velocity at time t. Use the formula to find a (in m s^{-2}) if:
(a) $v = 5$ ms^{-1}, $u = 1$ ms^{-1}, $t = 8$ s
(b) $v = 0.1$ ms^{-1}, $u = 0.02$ ms^{-1}, $t = 2$ s
(c) $v = 5.3$ ms^{-1}, $u = 3.2$ ms^{-1}, $t = 0.7$ s

2. Use the formula $s = vt - \frac{1}{2}at^2$ to calculate s (to 2 sf) given that
$$v = 27.27\,\text{m s}^{-1},$$
$$a = 9.81\,\text{ms}^{-2},$$
$$t = 1.73\,\text{s}.$$

3. The formula for the volume, V, of a sphere of radius r is $V = \frac{4}{3}\pi r^3$.
(a) Use this formula to calculate the volume of a sphere (to 3 sf) of radius 2 m.
(b) Make r the subject of the formula.
(c) Use part (b) to calculate the radius (to 3 sf) of a sphere of volume 200 mm^3.

4. Evaluate a^2b when $a = 5000$ and $b = 300$.

5. Given that $s = \frac{v^2 - u^2}{2a}$, find s when $u = 60$, $v = 80$ and $a = 400$.

6. If $\sqrt{\dfrac{py + q}{r}} = s$, find y (to 3 sf) if $p = 132$, $q = 251$, $r = 158$ and $s = 17$.

7. Make x the subject of these formulae:
(a) $mx + n = p$
(b) $a(x + b) = c$
(c) $\dfrac{x + p}{q} = r$
(d) $\dfrac{p(x + q)}{r} = t$
(e) $\dfrac{h}{x} = u$
(f) $\dfrac{k}{x + b} = w$
(g) $\dfrac{d}{ax + b} = c$
(h) $\dfrac{a}{x} + b = c$

8. Make the given variable the subject of the formula:
(a) w $\dfrac{aw + b}{c} = d$
(b) y $\dfrac{y + b}{x + t} = c$
(c) z $\dfrac{z}{a} = \dfrac{b}{c}$
(d) h $\dfrac{a}{h} = b$
(e) o $\dfrac{o}{h} = \dfrac{1}{2}$
(f) r $\dfrac{r}{t} = t$
(g) t $\dfrac{t + b}{a + c} = d$
(h) g $\dfrac{a}{g} = \dfrac{p}{q}$

Extended

9. Make x the subject of these formulae:
(a) $r + mx = nx$
(b) $ax + b = cx + d$
(c) $x = \dfrac{d + bx}{a}$
(d) $n - x = \dfrac{m + qx}{p}$
(e) $\dfrac{A}{x} = \dfrac{B}{x} + C$
(f) $\dfrac{ax}{x + b} = c$

10. Make the given variable the subject of these formulae:
(a) A $\dfrac{A + s}{A} = t$
(b) R $\dfrac{aR}{R + 1} = b$
(c) e $\dfrac{ae + b}{ce + d} = 1$
(d) p $\dfrac{ap}{bp + c} = d$
(e) Q $\dfrac{bQ}{Q + d} = c$
(f) x $\dfrac{\sqrt{ax - b}}{c} = d$
(g) y $\sqrt{\dfrac{my + n}{p}} = q$
(h) q $\dfrac{n - aq}{bq + m} = c$
(i) t $\sqrt{\dfrac{a - bt}{t}} = c$
(j) k $\left(\dfrac{ak}{k + b}\right)^2 = p$

16 Expanding and factorising

Expanding an expression means writing it without brackets.

Expanding simple expressions

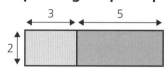

The total area in the diagram is $2 \times (3 + 5)$.
The area is made up of two rectangles – the small one has area 2×3 and the large one has area 2×5.
So $2 \times (3 + 5) = 2 \times 3 + 2 \times 5$

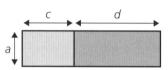

The total area is $a \times (c + d) = a(c + d)$.
It is made up of two rectangles – the small one has area $a \times c = ac$ and the large one has area $a \times d = ad$.
So $a(c + d) = ac + ad$

> Leave out the $\times$ symbol between two letters. So write $a \times b$ as ab.

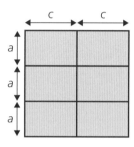

The total area is $3a \times 2c$.
It is made up of six rectangles, each with area $a \times c = ac$.
So $3a \times 2c = 6ac$

> The numbers can be dealt with separately from the letters. $3a \times 2c = (3 \times 2) \, ac = 6ac$

Example

Expand these expressions.

(a) $3(a + 2b)$
(b) $5(2m - 3n)$
(c) $2(6p + 7q) - 3(2p - 5q)$

    (a) $3(a + 2b) = 3a + 6b$
    (b) $5(2m - 3n) = 10m - 15n$
    (c) $2(6p + 7q) - 3(2p - 5q) = 12p + 14q - 6p + 15q = 6p + 29q$

> $15q$ comes from $(-3) \times (-5q)$

Example

Expand these expressions.

(a) $4a(2a + 3b)$
(b) $5p(2p - 5q)$
(c) $6s(2s + 7t) - 2s(5s - 2t)$

> $8a^2$ is shorthand for $8 \times a \times a$.

    (a) $4a(2a + 3b) = 8a^2 + 12ab$
    (b) $5p(2p - 5q) = 10p^2 - 25pq$
    (c) $6s(2s + 7t) - 2s(5s - 2t) = 12s^2 + 42st - 10s^2 + 4st = 2s^2 + 46st$

Expanding harder expressions

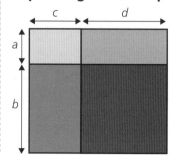

The total area is $(a + b) \times (c + d) = (a + b)(c + d)$.
It is made up of four smaller rectangles with areas ac, ad, bc and bd.

So $(a + b)(c + d) = ac + ad + bc + bd$

> Use the FOIL method
> **First terms** $a \times c = ac$
> **Outer terms** $a \times d = ad$
> **Inner terms** $b \times c = bc$
> **Last terms** $b \times d = bd$

Extended

Extended

Example
Expand and simplify $(2x + 3)(3x - 1)$.

First terms $2x \times 3x = 6x^2$ **O**uter terms $2x \times -1 = -2x$

Inner terms $3 \times 3x = 9x$ **L**ast terms $3 \times (-1) = -3$

$(2x + 3)(3x - 1) = 6x^2 + (-2x) + 9x + (-3) = 6x^2 + 7x - 3$

Example
Expand these expressions.

(a) $(x + 2)(x + 5)$ **(b)** $(x + 7)(x - 4)$

(c) $(x - 3)(x - 5)$ **(d)** $(2x + 3)(5x - 7)$

Use the FOIL method:

(a) $(x + 2)(x + 5)$ $= x \times x + x \times 5 + 2 \times x + 2 \times 5$
$= x^2 + 5x + 2x + 10 = x^2 + 7x + 10$

(b) $(x + 7)(x - 4)$ $= x \times x + x \times (-4) + 7 \times x + 7 \times (-4)$
$= x^2 - 4x + 7x - 28 = x^2 + 3x - 28$

(c) $(x - 3)(x - 5)$ $= x \times x + x \times (-5) + (-3) \times x + (-3) \times (-5)$
$= x^2 - 5x - 3x + 15 = x^2 - 8x + 15$

(d) $(2x + 3)(5x - 9)$ $= (2x) \times (5x) + (2x) \times (-9) + 3 \times (5x) + 3 \times (-9)$
$= 10x^2 - 18x + 15x - 27 = 10x^2 - 3x - 27$

> Be careful with expressions like $(x + 3)^2$.
> Write $(x + 3)^2$ as $(x + 3)(x + 3)$
> and so
> $(x + 3)^2 = x^2 + 3x + 3x + 9$
> $\qquad\quad = x^2 + 6x + 9$

Factorising simple expressions
When you expand $4a(2a + 3b)$ you get $8a^2 + 12ab$.

Factorising takes you back from $8a^2 + 12ab$ to $4a(2a + 3b)$.

Factorising $8a^2 + 12ab$:
- Find the highest common factor of $8a^2$ and $12ab$ by treating the numbers and each letter separately:

   The highest common factor of 8 and 12 is 4.
   The highest common factor of a^2 and a is a.
   There are no b's common to both $8a^2$ and $12ab$.
   So the highest common factor of $8a^2$ and $12ab$ is 4a.

- Express each term using the highest common factor, so $8a^2 = 4a \times 2a$
   and $12ab = 4a \times 3b$.

- Add these together to give $8a^2 + 12ab = 4a(2a + 3b)$

Factorising $15p^2q^3 + 12p^3q$:
- Find the highest common factor of $15p^2q^3$ and $12p^3q$ by treating the numbers and each letter separately:

   The highest common factor of 15 and 12 is 3.
   The highest common factor of p^2 and p^3 is p^2.
   The highest common factor of q^3 and q is q.
   So the highest common factor of $15p^2q^3$ and $12p^3q$ is $3p^2q$.

- Express each term using the highest common factor, so $15p^2q^3 = 3p^2q \times 5q^2$ and
   $12p^3q = 3p^2q \times 4p$.

- Add these together to give $15p^2q^3 + 12p^3q = 3p^2q(5q^2 + 4p)$

Example
Factorise these expressions.
(a) $9ab + 3b^2$
(b) $9x + 5x + 18y + 10y$
(c) $9r + 4s + 5r + 3s$

(a) $9ab$ and $3b^2$ have an HCF of $3b$.

$$9ab + 3b^2 = 3b(3a + b).$$

(b) $9x + 5x + 18y + 10y = 14x + 28y$ and $14x$ and $28y$ have an HCF of 14.

$$9x + 5x + 18y + 10y = 14x + 28y = 14(x + 2y)$$

(c) $9r + 4s + 5r + 3s = 14r + 7s$ and $14r$ and $7s$ have an HCF of 7.

$$9r + 4s + 5r + 3s = 14r + 7s = 7(2r + s)$$

Example
Factorise
$24x^2 - 16xy$.

$24x^2$ and $16xy$ have an HCF of $8x$.

$24x^2 - 16xy = 8x(3x - 2y)$

Factorising quadratic expressions

When you expand $(x + 2)(x + 5)$ you get $x^2 + 7x + 10$, which is a quadratic expression.

If you do the process in reverse you're factorising a quadratic.

Example
Factorise   **(a) $x^2 + 7x + 6$**   **(b) $x^2 + 3x - 28$**
             (c) $x^2 - 7x + 12$ **(d) $x^2 - 2x - 15$**

(a) $x^2 + 7x + 6$ Find two numbers that multiply to give 6 and add up to 7: 6 and 1.
     So $x^2 + 7x + 6 = (x + 6)(x + 1)$
(b) $x^2 + 3x - 28$ Find two numbers that multiply to give -28 and add up to 3: 7 and -4.
     So $x^2 + 3x - 28 = (x + 7)(x - 4)$
(c) $x^2 - 7x + 12$ Find two numbers that multiply to give 12 and add up to -7: -3 and -4.
     So $x^2 - 7x + 12 = (x - 3)(x - 4)$
(d) $x^2 - 2x - 15$ Find two numbers that multiply to give -15 and add up to -2: 3 and -5.
     So $x^2 - 2x - 15 = (x + 3)(x - 5)$

> When you have found the two factors always check they are correct by expanding them.

There are two special cases.
Case 1:   A quadratic expression with no middle term, "the difference of two squares"

Example
Factorise $x^2 - 16$.
     $x^2 - 16 = (x + 4)(x - 4)$

Example
Factorise $9x^2 - 16y^2$
     $9x^2 = (3x)^2$ and $16y^2 = (4y)^2$
     So again this is the difference of two squares.
     So $9x^2 - 16y^2 = (3x + 4y)(3x - 4y)$
     Notice that the two factors are the sum of the square roots times the difference of the
     square roots.

> NB $a^2 - b^2 = (a + b)(a - b)$
> So, for example,
> $100 - 49 = 10^2 - 7^2 = (10 + 7)(10 - 7)$
> and
> $25p^2 - 36q^2 = (5p)^2 - (6q)^2 = (5p + 6q)(5p - 6q)$

Extended

Case 2: A quadratic with no end term

When there is no end term the two terms in the quadratic have a common factor x.

So

$x^2 + 7x = x(x + 7)$

$2x^2 + 10x = 2x(x + 5)$

$20x^2 - 100x = 20x(x - 5)$

Factorising harder quadratic expressions

Example

Factorise $2x^2 + 7x + 6$.

(1) The brackets must be of the form $(2x + \text{\_\_})(x + \text{\_\_})$

(2) The missing numbers must multiply to give 6: 1 and 6 or 2 and 3.

(3) Try the four possible combinations.

$(2x + 1)(x + 6)$ gives $12x + x = 13x$

$(2x + 6)(x + 1)$ gives $2x + 6x = 8x$

$(2x + 2)(x + 3)$ gives $6x + 2x = 8x$

$(2x + 3)(x + 2)$ gives $4x + 3x = 7x$

> In **FOIL** the sum of the outer and inner terms give the x-term.

Only $(2x + 3)(x + 2)$ gives the $7x$ term in the middle, so

$2x^2 + 7x + 6 = (2x + 3)(x + 2)$

Example

Factorise $5x^2 - 16x + 3$.

(1) The brackets must be of the form $(5x - \text{\_\_})(x - \text{\_\_})$

(2) The missing numbers must multiply to give 3 so must be 1 and 3.

(3) Try the possible combinations.

Only $(5x - 1)(x - 3)$ gives the $-16x$ term in the middle, so

$5x^2 - 16x + 3 = (5x - 1)(x - 3)$

Factorising other expressions

Example

Factorise $ax + bx + 3ay + 3by$.

There is no factor common to all terms so factorise pairs of terms.

$ax + bx = (a + b)x$

$3ay + 3by = 3(a + b)y$

$(a + b)$ is a common factor.

So $ax + bx + 3ay + 3by = (a + b)x + 3(a + b)y = (a + b)(x + 3y)$

Example

Factorise $a^2 + 2ab + b^2$.

There is no factor common to all terms, but this is a quadratic expression.

The first terms must multiply to give a^2 and the last terms must multiply to give b^2, so try

$(a + b)(a + b)$.

$(a + b)(a + b) = a^2 + ab + ba + b^2$

$\qquad\qquad\quad = a^2 + 2ab + b^2$

> $ab = ba$

Extended

Exam question   CIE 0580 June '06 Paper 2 Q19

Factorise

  (a) $4x^2 - 9$

  (b) $4x^2 - 9x$

  (c) $4x^2 - 9x + 2$

(a) This is a quadratic with no middle term, "the difference of two squares", since

    $4x^2 - 9 = (2x)^2 - 3^2$

    So $4x^2 - 9 = (2x + 3)(2x - 3)$

(b) This is a quadratic with no end term.

    $4x^2 - 9x = x(4x - 9)$

(c) The only way to get "+2" and a negative middle term is with -1 and -2.

    $(2x - 1)(2x - 2)$ does not work, nor does $(x - 1)(4x - 2)$.

    Try $(4x - 1)(x - 2) = 4x^2 - 8x - x + 2 = 4x^2 - 9x + 2$

    So $4x^2 - 9x + 2 = (4x - 1)(x - 2)$

> Remember "square minus a square" = (sum of square roots) × (difference of square roots)

Questions

Extended

1. Expand these expressions.

  (a) $7(p + 3q)$

  (b) $6(5m - 7n)$

  (c) $3(5a + 2b) - 6(2a - 3b)$

2. Multiply out the brackets in these expressions.

  (a) $(2x + 1)(3x + 2)$ (b) $(5x + 2)(3x + 4)$

  (c) $(6t - 1)(2t - 3)$ (d) $(2y - 9)(3y - 1)$

  (e) $(7z - 1)(2z + 3)$ (f) $(9r - 2)(3r + 2)$

  (g) $(7e - 11)(2e + 1)$ (h) $(8q + 1)(5q - 3)$

  (i) $(3p - 1)(3p + 1)$ (j) $(7y + 2)(7y - 2)$

  (k) $(2k + 1)(k + 3)$ (l) $(2v - 1)(5v + 1)$

3. Multiply out the brackets and simplify these expressions.

  (a) $(x + 2)(x + 3)$ (b) $(x + 5)(x + 4)$

  (c) $(t + 1)(t + 2)$ (d) $(3q + 1)(2q - 1)$

  (e) $(5y + 2)(2y - 3)$ (f) $(5m - 1)(5m + 1)$

  (g) $(2y + 1)(2y - 1)$ (h) $(3p + 2)^2$

  (i) $(2q - 1)^2$ (j) $(5d + 2e)(2d - 3e)$

  (k) $(5p + 3q)(4p + q)$ (l) $(7s - 3t)(2s - t)$

4. Expand and simplify these expressions.

  (a) $(x + 3)^2$ (b) $(y + 5)^2$

  (c) $(y - 4)^2$ (d) $(z - 6)^2$

  (e) $(2w - 3)^2$ (f) $(5t - 2)^2$

  (g) $(3a + b)(2a + b)$ (h) $(3m - 2n)(5m - n)$

  (i) $(5p + 2q)(3p - 4q)$ (j) $(2x - 3y)(5x - 2y)$

  (k) $(3c + 2d)^2$ (l) $(5p - 3q)^2$

5. Factorise these quadratic expressions.

  (a) $x^2 + 9x + 18$ (b) $x^2 - x - 20$

  (c) $x^2 - 7x + 10$ (d) $x^2 + 3x - 40$

  (e) $x^2 - x - 42$ (f) $x^2 + 7x + 12$

  (g) $x^2 + 2x - 24$ (h) $x^2 - 16$

  (i) $x^2 + 3x$ (j) $x^2 - 25$

6. Factorise these quadratic expressions.

  (a) $x^2 - 5x - 6$ (b) $x^2 + 5x + 6$

  (c) $x^2 + 5x - 6$ (d) $x^2 - 5x + 6$

  (e) $x^2 - 4x - 60$ (f) $x^2 + 5x - 36$

  (g) $x^2 - 20x + 99$ (h) $x^2 - 1$

  (i) $x^2 + x - 132$ (j) $x^2 + 6x + 9$

  (k) $x^2 - 10x + 25$ (l) $x^2 - 100$

7. Factorise these quadratic expressions.

  (a) $x^2 + 7x + 12$ (b) $x^2 + 7x + 10$

  (c) $x^2 - 5x - 6$ (d) $x^2 - 5x + 6$

  (e) $2x^2 + 5x - 12$ (f) $3x^2 + 11x + 6$

  (g) $4x^2 + 12x + 5$ (h) $5x^2 + 13x + 8$

8. Factorise these quadratic expressions.

  (a) $a^2 + 5ab$ (b) $r^2 + 2r$

  (c) $t^2 - 36$ (d) $b^2 + 11b + 24$

  (e) $4p^2 + 20p + 9$ (f) $5q^2 - 8q - 4$

9. Factorise these quadratic expressions.

  (a) $x^2 + 3x + 2$ (b) $y^2 - 9$

  (c) $z^2 + 2z$ (d) $n^2 - n - 6$

  (e) $4p^2 - 8p - 5$ (f) $3q^2 - 8q + 4$

10. Factorise these quadratic expressions.

  (a) $x^2 - 9x + 20$ (b) $x^2 - 3x - 10$

  (c) $4x^2 - 11x + 6$ (d) $6x^2 - 13x - 5$

  (e) $8x^2 - 13x + 5$ (f) $6x^2 + 17x + 5$

17 Algebraic fractions

Adding and subtracting algebraic fractions

To add $\frac{3}{7} + \frac{2}{5}$ you find the LCM of 5 and 7, that is 35.

$$\frac{3}{7} + \frac{2}{5} = \frac{15}{35} + \frac{14}{35} = \frac{29}{35}$$

Algebraic fractions are added in the same way.

Example

Simplify $\frac{x + 1}{3} + \frac{x - 3}{4}$.

LCM of 3 and 4 is 12 so express both terms as fractions with denominator 12.

$$\frac{x + 1}{3} = \frac{4x + 4}{12} \quad \text{and} \quad \frac{x - 3}{4} = \frac{3x - 9}{12}$$

So

$$\frac{x + 1}{3} + \frac{x - 3}{4} = \frac{4x + 4}{12} + \frac{3x - 9}{12} = \frac{7x - 5}{12}$$

Example

Simplify $\frac{3(4x - 1)}{2} - \frac{2(5x + 3)}{3}$.

LCM of 2 and 3 is 6 so express both terms as fractions with denominator 6.

$$\frac{3(4x - 1)}{2} = \frac{36x - 9}{6} \quad \text{and} \quad \frac{2(5x + 3)}{3} = \frac{20x + 12}{6}$$

So

$$\frac{3(4x - 1)}{2} - \frac{2(5x + 3)}{3} = \frac{36x - 9}{6} - \frac{20x + 12}{6} = \frac{16x - 21}{6}$$

Example

Simplify $\frac{3}{1 - x} - \frac{2}{1 + x}$.

LCM of $1 - x$ and $1 + x$ is $(1 - x)(1 + x)$ so

$$\frac{3}{1 - x} = \frac{3(1 + x)}{(1 - x)(1 + x)} = \frac{3 + 3x}{(1 - x)(1 + x)} \quad \text{and} \quad \frac{2}{1 + x} = \frac{2(1 - x)}{(1 + x)(1 - x)} = \frac{2 - 2x}{(1 + x)(1 - x)}$$

So

$$\frac{3}{1 - x} - \frac{2}{1 + x}$$

$$= \frac{3 + 3x}{(1 - x)(1 + x)} - \frac{2 - 2x}{(1 + x)(1 - x)}$$

$$= \frac{1 + 5x}{(1 + x)(1 - x)}$$

Simplifying fractions contains quadratic expressions

Example

Factorise and simplify

(a) $\frac{x^2 - 4x}{x^2 - x - 12}$ (b) $\frac{x^2 - 7x + 12}{2x^2 - 7x + 3}$

(a) $\frac{x^2 - 4x}{x^2 - x - 12}$

$x^2 - 4x = x(x - 4)$

$x^2 - x - 12 = (x - 4)(x + 3)$

Hence

$$\frac{x^2 - 4x}{x^2 - x - 12} = \frac{x(x - 4)}{(x - 4)(x + 3)}$$

$$= \frac{x}{(x + 3)}$$

Extended

(b) $\dfrac{x^2 - 7x + 12}{2x^2 - 7x + 3}$

$x^2 - 7x + 12 = (x - 3)(x - 4)$

$2x^2 - 7x + 3 = (x - 3)(2x - 1)$

Hence

$\dfrac{x^2 - 7x + 12}{2x^2 - 7x + 3} = \dfrac{(x - 3)(x - 4)}{(x - 3)(2x - 1)}$

$\qquad\qquad = \dfrac{(x - 4)}{(2x - 1)}$

Exam question
CIE 0580 June '07 Paper 2 Q10

Write as a fraction in its simplest form
$$\frac{x - 3}{4} + \frac{4}{x - 3}.$$
LCM of 4 and $x - 3$ is $4(x - 3)$

$$\frac{x - 3}{4} + \frac{4}{x - 3} = \frac{(x - 3)(x - 3)}{4(x - 3)} + \frac{16}{4(x - 3)}$$

$$= \frac{(x - 3)(x - 3) + 16}{4(x - 3)}$$

$$= \frac{x^2 - 6x + 9 + 16}{4(x - 3)}$$

$$= \frac{x^2 - 6x + 25}{4(x - 3)}$$

Questions

1. Simplify, leaving your answers as fractions in their lowest form:

(a) $\dfrac{2x + 1}{3} + \dfrac{x + 1}{5}$

(b) $\dfrac{2x - 5}{2} + \dfrac{x + 3}{3}$

(c) $\dfrac{2x + 3}{4} + \dfrac{3x - 2}{6}$

(d) $\dfrac{3x + 1}{2} + \dfrac{x + 2}{7}$

(e) $\dfrac{3x + 5}{3} - \dfrac{x + 2}{4}$

(f) $\dfrac{5x + 1}{5} - \dfrac{3x - 2}{6}$

(g) $\dfrac{x - 1}{6} - \dfrac{5x + 3}{12}$

(h) $\dfrac{6x - 1}{4} - \dfrac{2x - 5}{5}$

2. Simplify, leaving your answers as fractions in their lowest form:

(a) $\dfrac{x}{2} + \dfrac{3x + 1}{5} + \dfrac{2x - 1}{10}$

(b) $\dfrac{x - 1}{4} + \dfrac{4x + 1}{5} + \dfrac{2x + 3}{20}$

(c) $\dfrac{x - 3}{2} + \dfrac{2x - 1}{3} + \dfrac{x + 1}{6}$

(d) $x + \dfrac{x}{2}$ (write as $\dfrac{2x}{2} + \dfrac{x}{2}$)

(e) $x + \dfrac{2x + 1}{2} + \dfrac{x}{3}$

(f) $x + 1 + \dfrac{3x + 2}{3} + \dfrac{x - 2}{4}$

3. Simplify, leaving your answers as fractions in their lowest form:

(a) $\dfrac{2}{x + 1} + \dfrac{3}{x + 2}$

(b) $\dfrac{3}{x + 2} + \dfrac{4}{x + 3}$

(c) $\dfrac{5}{x + 1} + \dfrac{7}{x - 1}$

(d) $\dfrac{5}{x + 3} - \dfrac{2}{x + 2}$

(e) $\dfrac{3}{2x + 3} + \dfrac{4}{3x - 1}$

(f) $\dfrac{5}{3x + 1} + \dfrac{4}{4x - 3}$

4. Simplify these fractions.

(a) $\dfrac{x^2 + 3x + 2}{x + 2}$

(b) $\dfrac{x^2 + 5x + 6}{x + 3}$

(c) $\dfrac{2x^2 + 3x + 1}{x + 1}$

(d) $\dfrac{x^2 + x - 12}{x + 4}$

(e) $\dfrac{x^2 - 7x + 10}{x - 2}$

(f) $\dfrac{4x^2 - 8x + 3}{2x - 3}$

(g) $\dfrac{x^2 - 1}{x - 1}$

(h) $\dfrac{25x^2 - 1}{5x + 1}$

18 Functions

If $A = \{1, 2, 3\}$ and $B = \{2, 3, 4\}$ then A is mapped onto B by the relation "add 1".

This can be shown on a mapping diagram:

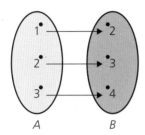

Set A is called the **domain** and set B is called the **range**.

If $x \in A$ then the mapping is $x \rightarrow x + 1$.

Notice that each element in A is mapped onto just one element in B.

The relation $x \rightarrow x + 1$ is a **one-to-one** relation.

Example
For the domain $A = \{-2, -1, 1, 2\}$ draw a diagram to show the mapping $x \rightarrow x^2$.

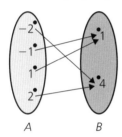

Notice that, in the mapping in this example, each element in the range is the image of more than one (i.e. "many") element in the domain: -2 and 2 are both mapped onto 4 and -1 and 1 are both mapped onto 1.

The relation $x \rightarrow x^2$ is a **many-to-one** relation.

One-to-one and many-to-one relations are called functions.

A **function** is a mapping in which each element in the domain has one, and only one image in the range.

Functions are usually denoted by the letters f, g etc so we can write

$$f : x \rightarrow x + 1 \quad \text{or} \quad f(x) = x + 1 \quad \text{and} \quad g : x \rightarrow x^2 \quad \text{or} \quad g(x) = x^2$$

Example
If $f(x) = x^3 + 3x^2 - 2$ then find (a) $f(-3)$ (b) $f(0.5)$
(a) $f(-3) = (-3)^3 + 3(-3)^2 - 2 = -2$

```
X³+3X²-2                    Math ▲

                      -2
```

(b) $f(0.5) = (0.5)^3 + 3(0.5)^2 - 2 = -1.125$

NB Use your calculator efficiently here. Either (i) use table or (ii) store -3 into memory X and then type in $x^3 + 3x^2 - 2$.

Extended

Composite functions

If $f(x) = x + 1$ and $g(x) = x^2$ then "gf" means "do f first, then g".
So $gf(x)$ means $g(f(x))$.

> Work from the inside outwards.

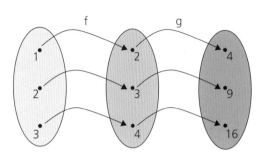

> So
> $f(1) = 2$ and $g(f(1)) = g(2) = 4$
> $f(2) = 3$ and $g(f(2)) = g(3) = 9$
> $f(3) = 4$ and $g(f(3)) = g(4) = 16$

Example

If $f(x) = x + 3$ and $g(x) = x^2$ then find:

(a) the value of x for which $f(x) = 8$

(b) the values of x for which $g(x) = 36$

(c) $f(g(4))$

(d) $g(f(x))$

    (a) Solving $f(x) = 8$ means solving $x + 3 = 8$. So $x = 5$.

    (b) Solving $g(x) = 36$ means solving $x^2 = 36$. So $x = 6$ or -6.

    (c) $g(4) = 4^2 = 16$ so $f(g(4)) = f(16) = 16 + 3 = 19$

    (b) $f(x) = x + 3$ so $g(f(x)) = g(x + 3) = (x + 3)^2$

Inverse functions

Consider the function $f(x) = \dfrac{3x + 1}{2}$ acting on the set $A = \{1, 2, 3\}$.

$$f : x \to \frac{3x + 1}{2}$$

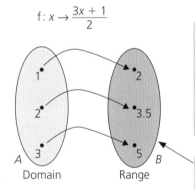

Domain   Range

> So:
> $f(1) = \dfrac{3 \times 1 + 1}{2} = 2$
>
> $f(2) = \dfrac{3 \times 2 + 1}{2} = 3.5$
>
> $f(3) = \dfrac{3 \times 3 + 1}{2} = 5$

> Notice that $f(x)$ is a "one-to-one function".

When $f(x)$ is a one-to-one function, as in this example, there is an inverse function, denoted by $f^{-1}(x)$ which "undoes" $f(x)$.

So $f^{-1}(x)$ does the following:

$f^{-1}(x)$

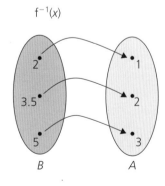

B A

> So, for example, $f^{-1}(2) = 1$ (1)
> but $2 = f(1)$ as above
> so replacing 2 with $f(1)$ in (1) gives
> $f^{-1}(f(1)) = 1$
> Similarly, $f(3) = 5$ and $f^{-1}(5) = 3$
> so $f^{-1}(f(3)) = 3$

> In fact it is true that, for all values of x:
> $f^{-1}(f(x)) = x$ and $f(f^{-1}(x)) = x$

Extended

Finding an inverse

To find the inverse of f(x):

- put f(x) = y and make x the subject of the formula in terms of y
- replace each y with x to find f^{-1}(x)

Example

Find the inverse of f(x) = $\dfrac{3x - 5}{2}$

- Putting f(x) = y: $y = \dfrac{3x - 5}{2}$

  Make x the subject of the formula: $x = \dfrac{2y + 5}{3}$

- Replacing y with x gives f^{-1}(x) = $\dfrac{2x + 5}{3}$

> Check your answer by substituting a numerical value for x e.g if x = 3,
> f(3) = 2 and f^{-1} (2) = 3

Example

Find the inverse of f(x) = $\dfrac{3}{x + 1}$ (for x > −1).

- Put f(x) = y: $y = \dfrac{3}{x + 1}$

  Rearrange: $yx + y = 3$ and so $x = \dfrac{3 - y}{y}$.

- Replace each y with x: f^{-1}(x) = $\dfrac{3 - x}{x}$ (for x > 0).

> Check:
> If x = 2, f(x) = 1
> and f^{-1} (1) = 2

Exam question   Adapted from CIE 0580 June '08 Paper 2 Q18

If f(x) = $x^3 - 3x^2 + 6x - 7$ and g(x) = 2x − 3

find:

(a) f(−1)

(b) gf(x)

(c) g^{-1}(x)

(a) Store −1 into memory X to give f(−1) = − 17.

(b) g(x) = 2x − 3

  g(f(x)) = 2f(x) − 3 = 2($x^3 - 3x^2 + 6x - 7$) − 3

  $= 2x^3 - 6x^2 + 12x - 14 - 3$

  $= 2x^3 - 6x^2 + 12x - 17$

(c) g (x) = 2x − 3

  y = 2x − 3

  y + 3 = 2x

  $x = \dfrac{y + 3}{2}$

  g^{-1}(x) = $\dfrac{x + 3}{2}$

Questions

1. If f(x) = $x^2 + 3$, find:

  (a) f(2)

  (b) f(−1)

  (c) a value of x such that f(x) = 3.

2. If f(x) = $\dfrac{x + 1}{x - 2}$ then find f^{-1}(x).

3. If f(x) = x^2 and g(x) = x + 1, find:

  (a) f(g(2))

  (b) f(g(x))

(c) a value of x such that f(g(x)) = 16

(d) g(g^{-1}(−3))

4. The functions f and g are as follows:

$$f : x \rightarrow 2x + 5$$

$$g : x \rightarrow 2 + \sqrt{x}$$

  (a) Calculate f(−3).

  (b) Given that f(a) = 17, find the value of a.

  (c) Find the inverse function of g.

19 Indices

2^5 5 is the index

2 is the base.

When you write $2 \times 2 \times 2 \times 2 \times 2$ as 2^5 you are using index notation.

When the index is a positive whole number, such as 5, 2^5 means "five 2s multiplied together".

The laws of indices

Examples

(a) $9^3 \times 9^4 = (9 \times 9 \times 9) \times (9 \times 9 \times 9 \times 9)$

$\qquad\qquad = 9 \times 9 \times 9 \times 9 \times 9 \times 9 \times 9$

$\qquad\qquad = 9^7$

To multiply powers of the same base **add** the indices.

$$9^3 \times 9^4 = 9^7$$

(b) $2^9 \div 2^4 = \dfrac{2^9}{2^4}$

$\qquad\qquad = \dfrac{{}^1\!\not2 \times {}^1\!\not2 \times {}^1\!\not2 \times {}^1\!\not2 \times 2 \times 2 \times 2 \times 2 \times 2}{{}^1\!\not2 \times {}^1\!\not2 \times {}^1\!\not2 \times {}^1\!\not2}$

$\qquad\qquad = 2^5$

To divide powers of the same base **subtract** the indices.

$$2^9 \div 2^4 = 2^5$$

(c) $(5^3)^4 = 5^3 \times 5^3 \times 5^3 \times 5^3$

$\qquad\quad = (5 \times 5 \times 5) \times (5 \times 5 \times 5) \times (5 \times 5 \times 5) \times (5 \times 5 \times 5)$

$\qquad\quad = 5 \times 5 \times 5 \times 5 \times 5 \times 5 \times 5 \times 5 \times 5 \times 5 \times 5 \times 5$

$\qquad\quad = 5^{12}$

To find a power of a power **multiply** the indices.

$$(5^3)^4 = 5^{12}$$

The three laws of indices can be written in a more general form.

- $a^m \times a^n = a^{m+n}$
- $a^m \div a^n = a^{m-n}$
- $(a^m)^n = a^{mn}$

Example

Simplify these expressions.

(a) $a^2 \times a^3$ (b) $(p^3)^4$ (c) $\dfrac{q^{11}}{q^2}$

(d) $h^3 \times h^7$ (e) $(t^2)^5$ (f) $\dfrac{r^4}{r^7}$

     (a) $a^2 \times a^3 = a^5$ (b) $(p^3)^4 = p^{12}$ (c) $q^{11} \div q^2 = q^9$

     (d) $h^3 \times h^7 = h^{10}$ (e) $(t^2)^5 = t^{10}$ (f) $r^4 \div r^7 = r^{4-7} = r^{-3}$

Example

Simplify these expressions.

(a) $(2x^2y^3)^4$ (b) $(3p^3q^5)^2$

     (a) $(2x^2y^3)^4 = 2^4(x^2)^4(y^3)^4 = 16x^8y^{12}$

     (b) $(3p^3q^5)^2 = 3^2(p^3)^2(q^5)^2 = 9p^6q^{10}$

Example

Calculate:

(a) 2^{10} (b) 3^4 (c) $\left(\dfrac{3}{2}\right)^3$

     (a) $2^{10} = 2 \times 2 \times 2 \times 2 \times 2 \times 2 \times 2 \times 2 \times 2 \times 2 = 1024$

     (b) $3^4 = 3 \times 3 \times 3 \times 3 = 81$

     (c) $\left(\dfrac{3}{2}\right)^3 = \dfrac{3}{2} \times \dfrac{3}{2} \times \dfrac{3}{2} = \dfrac{27}{8}$

Example
Express in the form a^n:
(a) $(11^3)^2 \times (11^2)^5$

(b) $\dfrac{(7^3)^4 \times 7^8}{(7^2)^5}$

(a) $(11^3)^2 = 11^{3 \times 2} = 11^6$ and $(11^2)^5 = 11^{2 \times 5} = 11^{10}$

So $(11^3)^2 \times (11^2)^5 = 11^6 \times 11^{10} = 11^{16}$

(b) $(7^3)^4 = 7^{3 \times 4} = 7^{12}$ and $(7^2)^5 = 7^{2 \times 5} = 7^{10}$

So
$$\frac{(7^3)^4 \times 7^8}{(7^2)^5} = \frac{7^{12} \times 7^8}{7^{10}}$$
$$= \frac{7^{20}}{7^{10}}$$
$$= 7^{20 - 10}$$
$$= 7^{10}$$

You will often use the powers of 2 up to 2^8, powers of 3 up to 3^4 and powers of 5 up to 5^4.
Knowing their values will help you.

Zero and negative indices
Look at this sequence: start with 16 and keep dividing by 2.

16   8   4   2   1   ½   ¼   ⅛

Write the sequence in index form:

2^4 2^3 2^2 2^1 2^0 2^{-1} 2^{-2} 2^{-3}

The index goes down by 1 each time you divide by 2.
Notice that $2^0 = 1$
- $a^0 = 1$ for all values of a.

Also $2^{-1} = ½$ $2^{-2} = ¼ = \dfrac{1}{2^2}$ and $2^{-3} = ⅛ = \dfrac{1}{2^3}$

A negative index can be replaced by "one over".
- $a^{-1} = \dfrac{1}{a}$

- $a^{-n} = \dfrac{1}{a^n}$ for all values of a and n.

Example
Calculate the following:
(a) 5^{-3} (b) $\left(\dfrac{3}{2}\right)^{-2}$ (c) 11^0

(a) $5^{-3} = \dfrac{1}{5^3} = \dfrac{1}{5 \times 5 \times 5} = \dfrac{1}{125}$

(b) $\left(\dfrac{3}{2}\right)^{-2} = \dfrac{1}{\left(\dfrac{3}{2}\right)^2} = \dfrac{1}{\dfrac{3}{2} \times \dfrac{3}{2}} = \dfrac{1}{\dfrac{9}{4}} = \dfrac{4}{9}$

(c) $11^0 = 1$

Example
Simplify $\dfrac{(3x^2y)^2 \times (2x^3y^2)^3}{(2x^5y^7)^2}$

$$\frac{(3x^2y)^2 \times (2x^3y^2)^3}{(2x^5y^7)^2} = \frac{9x^4y^2 \times 8x^9y^6}{4x^{10}y^{14}} = \frac{72x^{13}y^8}{4x^{10}y^{14}} = 18x^3y^{-6}$$

Fractional indices

Look at this sequence: start with 256 and keep taking square roots.

256   16   4   2 $\sqrt{2}$

Write the sequence in index form:

2^8 2^4 2^2 2^1 $2^{\frac{1}{2}}$

You divide the index by 2 each time you take a square root.

- Notice that $2^{\frac{1}{2}} = \sqrt{2}$

> In general $a^{\frac{1}{2}} = \sqrt{a}$ for all values of a.

What does $27^{\frac{1}{3}}$ mean?

$27^{\frac{1}{3}} = (3^3)^{\frac{1}{3}} = 3^{3 \times \frac{1}{3}} = 3^1$ which is the cube root of 27

- $a^{1/3} = \sqrt[3]{a}$ for all values of a

> In general $a^{\frac{1}{n}} = \sqrt[n]{a}$ for all values of a and n.

What does $8^{\frac{2}{3}}$ mean?

$8^{\frac{2}{3}} = \left(8^{\frac{1}{3}}\right)^2$ $8^{\frac{2}{3}} = (8^2)^{\frac{1}{3}}$

> In general $a^{\frac{m}{n}} = \sqrt[n]{a^m} = \left(\sqrt[n]{a}\right)^m$
> for all values of a and n.

$\quad = \left(\sqrt[3]{8}\right)^2$ $= 64^{\frac{1}{3}}$

$\quad = 2^2 = 4$ $= \sqrt[3]{64} = 4$

Example

Evaluate the following:

(a) $8^{\frac{4}{3}}$ **(b)** $16^{\frac{3}{4}}$ **(c)** $25^{-\frac{1}{2}}$

(d) $\left(\frac{27}{64}\right)^{\frac{1}{3}}$ **(e)** $\left(\frac{4}{9}\right)^{-\frac{3}{2}}$ **(f)** $\left(\sqrt{\frac{3}{2}}\right)^4$

(a) $8^{\frac{4}{3}} = \left(8^{\frac{1}{3}}\right)^4 = 2^4 = 16$ (b) $16^{\frac{3}{4}} = \left(16^{\frac{1}{4}}\right)^3 = 2^3 = 8$

(c) $25^{-\frac{1}{2}} = \dfrac{1}{25^{\frac{1}{2}}} = \dfrac{1}{5}$ (d) $\left(\dfrac{27}{64}\right)^{\frac{1}{3}} = \dfrac{27^{\frac{1}{3}}}{64^{\frac{1}{3}}} = \dfrac{3}{4}$

(e) $\left(\dfrac{4}{9}\right)^{-\frac{3}{2}} = \dfrac{1}{\left(\frac{4}{9}\right)^{\frac{3}{2}}} = \dfrac{1}{\left(\left(\frac{4}{9}\right)^{\frac{1}{2}}\right)^3} = \dfrac{1}{\left(\frac{2}{3}\right)^3} = \dfrac{1}{\frac{8}{27}} = \dfrac{27}{8}$ (f) $\left(\sqrt{\dfrac{3}{2}}\right)^4 = \left(\left(\dfrac{3}{2}\right)^{\frac{1}{2}}\right)^4 = \left(\dfrac{3}{2}\right)^2 = \dfrac{9}{4}$

Example

Find x where $32^x = 2$.

$32^x = (2^5)^x$ and $2 = 2^1$

So $2^{5x} = 2^1$.

Hence $5x = 1$ and so $x = \dfrac{1}{5}$.

Exam question

CIE 0580 November '06 Paper 2 Q7

Find the value of n in each of the following statements:

    (a) $32^n = 1$

    (b) $32^n = 2$

    (c) $32^n = 8$

    (a) $n = 0$ (since $a^0 = 1$ for all values of a)

    (b) $32 = 2^5$ so $32^n = (2^5)^n = 2^{5n}$

       Since $32^n = 2$ it follows that $2^{5n} = 2 = 2^1$.

       Hence $5n = 1$ and so $n = \dfrac{1}{5}$

> Since $2^5 = 32$ it follows that $32^{\frac{1}{5}} = 2$ and so $n = \dfrac{1}{5}$ without any of this working.

    (c) As in (b), since $32^n = 8$, $2^{5n} = 8 = 2^3$. Hence $5n = 3$ and so $n = \dfrac{3}{5}$.

Extended

Exam question

CIE 0580 June '07 Paper 2 Q17

(a) If $\sqrt{32} = 2^p$, find the value of p.

(b) If $\sqrt[3]{\dfrac{1}{8}} = 2^q$, find the value of q.

(a) $\sqrt{32} = 32^{\frac{1}{2}}$

$32 = 2^5$ so $\sqrt{32} = (2^5)^{\frac{1}{2}} = 2^{\frac{5}{2}}$

So $p = \dfrac{5}{2}$

(b) $\sqrt[3]{\dfrac{1}{8}} = \left(\dfrac{1}{8}\right)^{\frac{1}{3}} = \dfrac{1^{\frac{1}{3}}}{8^{\frac{1}{3}}} = \dfrac{1}{2} = 2^{-1}$

so $q = -1$

Questions

1. Simplify these expressions.

(a) $a^2 \times a^3$ (b) $b^3 \times b^{14}$

(c) $c^6 \times c^5$ (d) $x^6 \times x^7$

(e) $y^9 \div y^2$ (f) $z^{11} \div z^4$

(g) $(q^3)^4$ (h) $(w^2)^6$

(i) $(r^2)^3 \div r^4$ (j) $(s^5)^3 \times s^6$

(k) $\dfrac{t^2 \times t^5}{t^3}$ (l) $\dfrac{(w^3)^4 \times w^6}{w^2}$

2. Find a when:

(a) $2^3 \times 2^a = 2^7$ (b) $x^5 \times x^a = x^6$

(c) $y^2 \times y^a = y^2$ (d) $r^a \div r^{11} = r^9$

(e) $s^a \div s^9 = s^7$ (f) $2^9 \div 2^a = 2^2$

(g) $(3^5)^a = 3^{20}$ (h) $(u^a)^a = u^9$

(i) $(x^a)^{a+1} = x^{42}$

3. Simplify these fractions.

(a) $\dfrac{(2x^8) \times (6x^5)}{4x^9}$ (b) $\dfrac{(4y^6) \times (5y^7)}{10y^{11}}$

(c) $\dfrac{(8z^2) \times (3z^3)}{2z^4}$ (d) $\dfrac{(6a^3) \times (4a^9)}{(2a^2) \times (3a^8)}$

(e) $\dfrac{(12c^3) \times (4c^9)}{(2c^2) \times (3c^6)}$ (f) $\dfrac{(10h^2) \times (18h^5)}{(5h^4) \times (3h)}$

4. Simplify these fractions.

(a) $\dfrac{(4a^3b^4) \times (10a^2b^5)}{5a^4b^2}$ (b) $\dfrac{(6mn^2) \times (10m^3n^4)}{4mn^2}$

(c) $\dfrac{(2r^2t^4) \times (10r^5t^3)}{5r^2t^5}$ (d) $\dfrac{(3g^2h^5) \times (2g^3h^6)}{6g^3h}$

5. Simplify these expressions.

(a) $(2x^2y)^3$ (b) $(3x^3y^4)^2$

(c) $(8x^2y^3)^2$ (d) $(5x^2y^5)^3$

(e) $(9x^6y^7)^2$ (f) $(8x^7y^3)^2$

(g) $(2x^2y^3)^4 \times (3x^2y^3)^3$ (h) $(2x^3y^5)^3 \times (5x^3y^4)^2$

6. Calculate the values of these expressions.

(a) 2^6 (b) 3^4 (c) 5^3

(d) 11^2 (e) 2^{-3} (f) 10^{-2}

(g) 19^0 (h) 13^2 (i) 4^{-3}

(j) $\left(\dfrac{1}{2}\right)^3$ (k) $\left(\dfrac{2}{3}\right)^2$ (l) $\left(\dfrac{5}{3}\right)^4$

(m) $\left(\dfrac{1}{2}\right)^{-2}$ (n) $\left(\dfrac{2}{5}\right)^{-3}$ (o) $\left(\dfrac{2}{3}\right)^{-4}$

Extended

7. Find x when:

(a) $32^x = 2$ (b) $81^x = 3$ (c) $125^x = 5$

(d) $49^x = 7$ (e) $121^x = 11$ (f) $27^x = 3$

(g) $243^x = 3$ (h) $256^x = 16$ (i) $3^x = \dfrac{1}{3}$

(j) $81^x = \dfrac{1}{3}$ (k) $125^x = \dfrac{1}{5}$ (l) $512^x = \dfrac{1}{2}$

8. Evaluate these expressions without using decimals. Show all working clearly.

(a) 3^{-4} (b) 5^{-3} (c) 7^{-2}

(d) $8^{\frac{1}{3}}$ (e) $16^{\frac{3}{4}}$ (f) $25^{\frac{3}{2}}$

(g) $\left(\dfrac{3}{4}\right)^2$ (h) $\left(\dfrac{27}{64}\right)^{\frac{1}{3}}$ (i) $\left(\dfrac{16}{625}\right)^{\frac{1}{4}}$

20 Solving linear equations

In a linear equation the highest power of x is 1.

$3x + 2 = 17$ is a linear equation.

When you solve the equation you find the value of x which makes the left-hand side of the equation equal to the right-hand side.

The solution of $3x + 2 = 17$ is $x = 5$ since $3 \times 5 + 2 = 17$.

You solve an equation by doing the same operation to both sides.

Example
Solve the equation $3x - 5 = 16$.

$3x - 5 = 16$	Add 5 to both sides.
$3x = 21$	Divide both sides by 3.
$x = 7$	

Check:
$3 \times 7 - 5 = 16$

Example
Solve the equation $2(x + 4) = 14$.

$2(x + 4) = 14$	Expand the brackets.
$2x + 8 = 14$	Subtract 8 from both sides.
$2x = 6$	Divide both sides by 2.
$x = 3$	

Check:
$2(3 + 4) = 14$

Example
Solve the equation $\frac{3x}{4} = 12$

$\frac{3x}{4} = 12$	Clear the fractions by multiplying both sides by 4.
$3x = 48$	Divide both sides by 3.
$x = 16$	

Check:
$\frac{3 \times 16}{4} = \frac{48}{4} = 12$

Cross multiplying

If you have an equation of the form $\frac{a}{b} = \frac{c}{d}$ with a **single fraction** only on each side you can "**cross multiply**" to give $ad = bc$

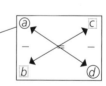

For example:

$$\frac{x + 1}{2} = \frac{x}{5}$$
$$5(x + 1) = 2x$$
$$5x + 5 = 2x$$
Hence $3x = -5$
$$x = -\frac{5}{3}$$

To solve a linear equation:

Step 1	Clear the fractions.
Step 2	Expand the brackets
Step 3	Put all the x-terms on one side of the equation.
Step 4	Simplify the equation.
Step 5	Check your solution.

Example

Solve $\dfrac{3x + 1}{2} = 11$

$\dfrac{3x + 1}{2} = 11$ Clear the fractions.

$3x + 1 = 22$ Subtract 1 from both sides.

$3x = 21$ Divide both sides by 3.

$x = 7$

Example

Find x if $\dfrac{1}{8} + \dfrac{1}{3} = \dfrac{x}{3}$

$\dfrac{1}{8} + \dfrac{1}{3} = \dfrac{x}{3}$ Clear the fractions by multiplying both sides by 24.

$3 + 8 = 8x$ Simplify.

$8x = 11$ Divide both sides by 8.

$x = \dfrac{11}{8} = 1\dfrac{3}{8}$

Example

Find x if $\dfrac{7(x + 2) - 1}{8} = 6$

$\dfrac{7(x + 2) - 1}{8} = 6$ Clear the fractions.

$7(x + 2) - 1 = 48$ Expand the brackets.

$7x + 14 - 1 = 48$ Simplify.

$7x + 13 = 48$ Subtract 13 from both sides.

$7x = 35$ Divide both sides by 7.

$x = 5$

Solving simultaneous equations by elimination

Apples cost a cents and bananas cost b cents.

Avni buys 3 apples and 1 banana and pays 90c.

Cost of 3 apples $= 3a$ cents and cost of 1 banana $= b$ cents.

So $3a + b = 90$ (1)

Parmjit buys 1 apple and 2 bananas and pays 80c.

Cost of 1 apple $= a$ cents and cost of 2 bananas $= 2b$ cents.

So $a + 2b = 80$ (2)

Equations (1) and (2) are called **simultaneous equations** because they have a common solution.

You can solve simultaneous equations by **elimination**.

$3a + b = 90$ (1)
$a + 2b = 80$ (2)

Multiply equation (1) by 2 so that both equations have a $2b$ term.

$6a + 2b = 180$ $\qquad$ (3)

Subtract equation (2) from equation (3) to eliminate the $2b$ terms.

$(6a + 2b) - (a + 2b) = 180 - 80$
$\qquad\qquad 5a = 100$, so $a = 20$

Use the value of a in equation (1) to find b.

$3 \times 20 + b = 90$, so $b = 30$

> Check the solution.
> Avni pays $3 \times 20 + 1 \times 30 = 90$
> Parmjit pays $1 \times 20 + 2 \times 30 = 80$

An apple costs 20c and a banana costs 30c.

In the elimination method you have to get two equations like this:

1 Same coefficients and same signs or **2 Same coefficients but different signs**

$$3x + 2y = 19 \quad (1)$$
$$6x + 2y = 34 \quad (2)$$

$$2x + 6y = 26 \quad (1)$$
$$7x - 6y = 10 \quad (2)$$

In this case **subtract**
the equations: (2) − (1)
$6x - 3x + 2y - 2y = 34 - 19$

> SAME SIGNS SUBTRACT

$$3x = 15$$
$$x = 5$$

Put $x = 5$ in equation (1)
$3 \times 5 + 2y = 19$
$15 + 2y = 19$
$2y = 4$
$y = 2$

In this case **add** the
equations: (1) + (2)
$2x + 7x + 6y - 6y = 26 + 10$

> DIFFERENT SIGNS ADD

$$9x = 36$$
$$x = 4$$

Put $x = 4$ in equation (1)
$2 \times 4 + 6y = 26$
$8 + 6y = 26$
$6y = 18$
$y = 3$

Example

Solve this pair of simultaneous equations:
$$3x + y = 13 \qquad (1)$$
$$7x - y = 27 \qquad (2)$$

In this case the coefficients of y are already the same (but with different signs).

The coefficients have **d**ifferent signs so **add** the two equations.

$10x = 40$ and so $x = 4$

Replace x with 4 in equation (1) to give:
$\qquad 12 + y = 13$
So $\qquad y = 1$

> Check using equation (2)
> $7 \times 4 - 1 = 27$

The solution is $x = 4$, $y = 1$

Example

Solve these simultaneous equations:
$$4x + 3y = 27 \qquad (1)$$
$$2x + 5y = 31 \qquad (2)$$

Multiply (2) by 2 (to get $4x$ in both equations)

$2x + 5y = 31$ $\qquad \times 2$

$4x + 10y = 62$ $\qquad$ (3)

Now the equations are:

$\qquad 4x + 3y = 27$ $\qquad$ (1)

$\qquad 4x + 10y = 62$ $\qquad$ (3)

The x-terms have the same sign so *subtract* equation (1) from equation (3)

$\qquad 7y = 35$ and so $y = 5$

Substitute for y in equation (1):

$\qquad 4x + 15 = 27$

and so $\qquad 4x = 12$

$\qquad\qquad x = 3$

The solution is $x = 3$, $y = 5$

> Check using equation (2)
> $2 \times 3 + 5 \times 5 = 31$

Example

Solve these simultaneous equations:

$2x - 3y = 8$ $\qquad$ (1)

$3x + 2y = 25$ $\qquad$ (2)

Multiply (1) by 2 and (2) by 3 (to get $6y$ in both equations)

$4x - 6y = 16$ $\qquad$ (3)

$9x + 6y = 75$ $\qquad$ (4)

The y-terms have **d**ifferent signs so a**dd** equations (3) and (4)

$\qquad 13x = 91$ and so $x = 7$

Substitute for x in equation (2) to give

$21 + 2y = 25$ and so $2y = 4$

$\qquad\qquad y = 2$

> Check using equation (1)
> $2 \times 7 - 3 \times 2 = 8$

The solution is $x = 7$, $y = 2$

The coordinates of the point where two lines cross is the solution of a pair of simultaneous equations.

Extended

Exam question $\qquad\qquad$ CIE 0580 June '08 Paper 2 Q16

Find the coordinates of the point of intersection of the straight lines:

$2x + 3y = 11$ $\qquad$ (1)

$3x - 5y = -12$ $\qquad$ (2)

$\quad 2x + 3y = 11$ $\qquad$ (1) $\times 3$

$\quad 3x - 5y = -12$ $\qquad$ (2) $\times 2$

$\quad 6x + 9y = 33$ $\qquad$ (3)

$\quad 6x - 10y = -24$ $\qquad$ (4)

Subtract (4) from (3)

$19y = 57$, so $y = 3$

Put $y = 3$ in (1)

$2x + 9 = 11$

$\quad 2x = 2$, so $x = 1$

The point of intersection is (1, 3).

Solving simultaneous equations by substitution

Example

Solve:

$$2x + 5y = 19 \qquad (1)$$
$$y = x + 1 \qquad (2)$$

Equation (2) gives y in terms of x so substitute $(x + 1)$ for y in equation (1).

$$2x + 5(x + 1) = 19$$
$$7x + 5 = 19$$
$$7x = 14, \text{ so } x = 2$$

Put $x = 2$ in equation $\qquad$ (2)

$$y = 2 + 1 = 3$$

> Check using equation (1)
> $2 \times 2 + 5 \times 3 = 19$

The solution is $x = 2$, $y = 3$

Example

Solve:

$$3x + 2y = 13 \qquad (1)$$
$$y = x - 6 \qquad (2)$$

Substitute $(x - 6)$ for y in (1)

$$3x + 2(x - 6) = 13$$
$$5x - 12 = 13$$
$$5x = 25, \text{ so } x = 5$$

> Check using equation (1)
> $3 \times 5 + 2 \times (-1) = 13$

Put $x = 5$ in (2)

$$y = 5 - 6 = -1$$

The solution is $x = 5$, $y = -1$

Solving simultaneous equations graphically

To solve $y = 2x + 1$ and $x + y = 4$ plot both lines on the same diagram.

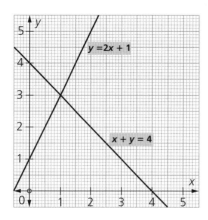

The point of intersection, $(1, 3)$ is the solution so $x = 1$, $y = 3$.

Questions

1. The three angles in a triangle are a, $a + 20$ and $a + 25$.

(a) Write down an equation involving a.

(b) Solve this equation to find a.

(Triangle with angles labelled $a + 25$ at top, a at bottom left, $a + 20$ at bottom right)

2. Three consecutive whole numbers add up to 144. If the lowest number is n then:

(a) write down an expression for the other two numbers in terms of n

(b) write down an equation involving n

(c) find n and hence find the other two numbers.

3. Solve the following equations.

(a) $3(x - 1) = 2(x + 1)$

(b) $2(5x + 2) = 6(3x - 2)$

(c) $5(7x - 3) = 4(9x - 4)$

(d) $3(4x + 5) + 7 = 2(3x + 23)$

(e) $7(4x + 9) + 3 = 5(x + 4)$

(f) $4(2x - 3) = 2(2x + 1) + 10$

4. Solve the following equations.

(a) $\dfrac{15}{x} = 5$

(b) $\dfrac{6}{x} = 2$

(c) $\dfrac{42}{x + 3} = 6$

(d) $\dfrac{35}{2x + 1} = 5$

(e) $\dfrac{24}{5x + 3} = 3$

(f) $\dfrac{12}{5x + 1} = 2$

5. Solve these simultaneous equations by elimination.

(a) $2x + y = 11$
   $3x - y = 14$

(b) $3u + 2v = 10$
   $7u - v = 29$

(c) $11p + 3q = 71$
   $5p - q = 37$

(d) $9a + 2b = 41$
   $5a - 4b = 33$

(e) $7p - 3q = 15$
   $5p + 2q = 19$

(f) $13b - 7c = 47$
   $7b - 9c = 41$

6. Solve these simultaneous equations (by the substitution method):

(a) $5m + 3n = 27$
   $m = 7 - n$

(b) $2p + 7q = 3$
   $p = 6 + q$

In parts (c) − (f) first rearrange one of the equations.

(c) $u + 2v = 7$
   $2u + 3v = 11$

(d) $3p + 2q = 21$
   $p - 3q + 4 = 0$

(e) $7r + 2s = 17$
   $r - 3s = 9$

(f) $5x - 7y + 5 = 26$
   $x - y - 9 = 0$

7. A man buys 5 first class tickets and 2 second class tickets which cost him €246. Another man buys 2 first class and 3 second class tickets which cost him €149.

Let the price of a first class ticket be €x and the price of a second class ticket be €y.

(a) Write down a pair of simultaneous equations involving x and y.

(b) Find x and y.

8. Two numbers p and q (where p is the bigger number) are such that their sum is 95 and their difference is 21.

(a) Write down a pair of simultaneous equations involving p and q.

(b) Find p and q.

9. A man buys three student tickets and five adult tickets which costs him \$62. Another man buys seven student tickets and three adult tickets which cost him \$71. Let the price of a student ticket be \$$s$ and the price of an adult ticket be \$$a$.

(a) Write down a pair of simultaneous equations involving s and a.

(b) Find s and a.

10. By looking at points of intersection of the straight lines shown on the graph, solve the following pairs of simultaneous equations.

(a) $y - x - 5 = 0$
   $y - 2x = 1$

(b) $y - x = 5$
   $y + x = 1$

(c) $2y + x = 12$
   $y - 1 = 2x$

(d) $3y + 5x = -30$
   $y - 2x = 1$

(e) $x + y - 1 = 0$
   $y + 39 = 7x$

(f) $2y = 12 - x$
   $y - 7x = -39$

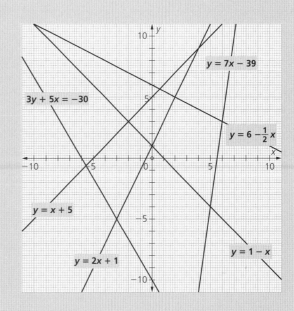

21 Solving quadratic equations

Solving quadratic equations by factorising

If you can factorise a quadratic equation you can solve it.

Example

Solve $x^2 + 6x + 8 = 0$

$$x^2 + 6x + 8 = 0$$
$$(x + 2)(x + 4) = 0$$
Either $x + 2 = 0$
or $x + 4 = 0$
so $x = -2$ or -4

> For the factors you need two numbers that **multiply** to give 8 and **add** up to 6 since the 8 has a + sign.

> If two numbers multiply to give 0 then at least one of them must be 0.

> Check
> $(-2)^2 + (6 \times -2) + 8$
> $= 4 - 12 + 8 = 0$
> and
> $(-4)^2 + (6 \times -4) + 8$
> $= 16 - 24 + 8 = 0$

Example

Solve $x^2 + 5x - 24 = 0$

$$x^2 + 5x - 24 = 0$$
$$(x + 8)(x - 3) = 0$$
Either $x + 8 = 0$ giving $x = -8$
or $x - 3 = 0$ giving $x = 3$

> Find two numbers which **multiply** to give -24 and **add** to give 5, that is 8 and -3.

> Check
> $(-8)^2 + 5(-8) - 24$
> $= 64 - 40 - 24 = 0$
> and
> $(3)^2 + 5(3) - 24$
> $= 9 + 15 - 24 = 0$

Two special cases

Case 1 Quadratic with no middle term, "the difference of two squares"

Example

Solve $x^2 - 16 = 0$

$$x^2 - 16 = 0$$
$$(x - 4)(x + 4) = 0$$
Either $x - 4 = 0$
so $x = 4$
or $x + 4 = 0$
so $x = -4$

> The common mistake is to write $x^2 = 16$ and so $x = 4$, which is only one of the solutions.

> Check
> $4^2 - 16 = 0$
> $(-4)^2 - 16 = 0$

Extended

Case 2 Quadratic with no end term

Example

Solve $x^2 - 5x = 0$

$$x^2 - 5x = 0$$
$$x(x - 5) = 0$$
either $x = 0$
or $x - 5 = 0$ giving $x = 5$

The common mistake is to divide by x and get
$$x - 5 = 0.$$

x is a common factor

Check $5^2 - 5 \times 5 = 0$ and $0^2 - 5 \times 0 = 0$

Solving harder quadratic equations

Example

Solve $3x^2 - 14x + 8 = 0$

$$3x^2 - 14x + 8 = 0$$

The factors are $(3x \underline{})(x \underline{})$

Trial and error gives $3x^2 - 14x + 8 = (3x - 2)(x - 4)$

So if $(3x - 2)(x - 4) = 0$ then
either $3x - 2 = 0$ giving $x = \frac{2}{3}$
or $x - 4 = 0$ giving $x = 4$

$8 = 1 \times 8$ or 2×4
and you need $-14x$
$4 \times 3x + 2 \times x = 14x$

Check
$$3\left(\frac{2}{3}\right)^2 - 14 \times \frac{2}{3} + 8$$
$$= \frac{4}{3} - \frac{28}{3} + 8 = 0$$
$$3(4)^2 - 14 \times 4 + 8$$
$$= 48 - 56 + 8 = 0$$

Solving quadratic equations by completing the square

$$(x + 3)^2 = (x + 3)(x + 3) = x^2 + 3x + 3x + 9 = x^2 + 6x + 9$$

Since $x^2 + 6x + 11 = x^2 + 6x + 9 + 2$ it follows that $x^2 + 6x + 11 = (x + 3)^2 + 2$.

If you write $x^2 + 6x + 11$ in the form $(x + 3)^2 + 2$ you are "completing the square".

To solve a quadratic equation using a non-factorisation method you only need to learn to use one of the following methods (completing the square **or** the quadratic formula).

This is the square.
"$+3$" is obtained by halving "$+6$" in "$+6x$"

This is the completing of the square.

Example

Complete the square on $x^2 + 8x + 21$.

$$x^2 + 8x + 21 = (x + 4)^2 + 5$$

$8 \div 2 = 4$

$21 = 4^2 + 5$

Example

Complete the square on $x^2 - 8x + 3$.

$$x^2 - 8x + 3 = (x - 4)^2 - 13$$

$-8 \div 2 = -4$

$3 = (-4)^2 - 13$

Example

Complete the square on $x^2 - x + 1$.

$$x^2 - x + 1 = \left(x - \tfrac{1}{2}\right)^2 + \tfrac{3}{4}$$

-1 divided by $2 = -\tfrac{1}{2}$

$1 = \left(-\tfrac{1}{2}\right)^2 + \tfrac{3}{4}$

Example

Solve $x^2 + 8x + 5 = 0$ by completing the square.

$$x^2 + 8x + 5 = (x + 4)^2 - 11$$

$8 \div 2 = 4$

$5 = 4^2 - 11$

So you need to solve $(x + 4)^2 - 11 = 0$

Hence $(x + 4)^2 = 11$

So $x + 4 = \pm\sqrt{11}$ and so $x = -4 \pm \sqrt{11}$. $x = -0.683$ or $x = -7.32$ (to 3sf).

Solving quadratic equations by using the quadratic formula

The quadratic formula states that the solutions to the equation $ax^2 + bx + c = 0$

are $\dfrac{-b + \sqrt{b^2 - 4ac}}{2a}$ and $\dfrac{-b - \sqrt{b^2 - 4ac}}{2a}$.

The two solutions are usually combined in the form $\dfrac{-b \pm \sqrt{b^2 - 4ac}}{2a}$ where $\pm$ means "plus or minus".

To use this method replace the letters a, b, and c with the numbers that come from the particular equation you want to solve.

> Take care when using your calculator to work out solutions to the quadratic equation.

Example

Solve the equation $3x^2 - 2x - 7 = 0$.

The equation can't be factorised so solve it using the formula.

$$x = \frac{-b \pm \sqrt{b^2 - 4ac}}{2a}$$

Write down the values of a, b and c.

$a = 3$, $b = -2$, $c = -7$

Substitute these values in the formula.

$$x = \frac{2 \pm \sqrt{(-2)^2 - 4 \times 3 \times -7}}{6}$$

$$= \frac{2 \pm \sqrt{88}}{6}$$

$$= \frac{2 \pm 9.3808\ldots}{6}$$

$$= 1.90 \text{ or } -1.23 \text{ to 3 sf}$$

Problems involving quadratic equations

Exam question   CIE 0580 June '07 Paper 4 Q8

A packet of sweets contains chocolates and toffees.

(a) There are x chocolates which have a total mass of 105 grams.
   Write down, in terms of x, the mean mass of a chocolate.

(b) There are $x + 4$ toffees which have a total mass of 105 grams.
   Write down, in terms of x, the mean mass of a toffee.

(c) The difference between the two mean masses in parts (a) and (b) is 0.8 grams. Write down an equation in x and show that it simplifies to $x^2 + 4x - 525 = 0$.

(d) (i)   Factorise $x^2 + 4x - 525$.
   (ii) Write down the solutions of $x^2 + 4x - 525 = 0$.

(e) Write down the total number of sweets in the packet.

(f)   Find the mean mass of a sweet in the packet.

(a) Mean mass $= \dfrac{\text{total mass}}{\text{number of chocolates}} = \dfrac{105}{x}$

(b) Mean mass $= \dfrac{\text{total mass}}{\text{number of toffees}} = \dfrac{105}{x + 4}$

(c) Difference is 0.8 so $\dfrac{105}{x} - \dfrac{105}{x + 4} = 0.8$

$$\dfrac{105(x + 4)}{x(x + 4)} - \dfrac{105x}{x(x + 4)} = \dfrac{420}{x(x + 4)}$$

$$\text{so } \dfrac{420}{x(x + 4)} = 0.8$$

$$\dfrac{420}{x(x + 4)} = \dfrac{4}{5}$$

$$5 \times 420 = 4x(x + 4)$$

$$2100 \quad = 4x^2 + 16x$$

$$4x^2 + 16x - 2100 = 0 \qquad \text{(dividing both sides by 4)}$$

$$x^2 + 4x - 525 = 0$$

(d) (i) $x^2 + 4x - 525 = (x + 25)(x - 21)$ $\longleftarrow$ $\boxed{525 = 25 \times 21}$

   (ii) $x = -25$ or $x = 21$

(e) x is number of chocolates and cannot be negative. So there are 21 chocolates and $x + 4 = 25$ toffees. So there are 46 sweets in total.

(f) Mean mass $= \dfrac{\text{total mass of all sweets}}{\text{number of sweets}} = \dfrac{210}{46} = 4.57$ g (to 3 sf)

Extended

Exam question
CIE 0580 June '06 Paper 4 Q8 b

The diagram shows a right-angled triangle.

The lengths of the sides are given in terms of y.

(a) Show that $2y^2 - 8y - 3 = 0$.

(b) Solve the equation $2y^2 - 8y - 3 = 0$, giving your
answers to 2 decimal places.

(c) Calculate the area of the triangle.

$2y - 1$ y Not to scale

$y + 2$

(a) Using Pythagoras' theorem gives
$$(y + 2)^2 + y^2 = (2y - 1)^2$$
$$(y + 2)(y + 2) + y^2 = (2y - 1)(2y - 1)$$
$$y^2 + 2y + 2y + 4 + y^2 = 4y^2 - 2y - 2y + 1$$
$$2y^2 - 8y - 3 = 0$$

(b) $a = 2,\quad b = -8,\quad c = -3$.

So $y = \dfrac{8 \pm \sqrt{8^2 - 4(2 \times -3)}}{4} = \dfrac{8 \pm \sqrt{64 + 24}}{4} = \dfrac{8 \pm \sqrt{88}}{4}$

So $y = \dfrac{8 \pm \sqrt{88}}{4} = 4.34520788$ or -0.34520788

(c) y is the height of the triangle so must be positive so $y = 4.34520788$

So the base of the triangle is $y + 2 = 6.34520788$

Area of triangle $= \frac{1}{2} \times$ base $\times$ height $= \frac{1}{2} \times 4.34520788 \times 6.34520788 = 13.8$ (to 3 sf)

Questions

1. Solve these equations.
   (a) $x^2 + 7x + 12 = 0$ (b) $y^2 + 13y + 22 = 0$
   (c) $m^2 - 5m - 6 = 0$ (d) $a^2 - 5a + 6 = 0$
   (e) $z^2 - 4z - 12 = 0$ (f) $z^2 + 2z + 1 = 0$
   (g) $c^2 + 15c + 36 = 0$ (h) $t^2 - 18t + 81 = 0$
   (i) $r^2 - 6r = 0$ (j) $t^2 + 11t = 0$
   (k) $w^2 - 3w = 0$ (l) $k^2 + k = 0$

2. Solve the following equations by completing the
   square (leaving square roots in your answers).
   (a) $x^2 + 2x - 1 = 0$ (b) $x^2 - 4x - 3 = 0$
   (c) $x^2 + 12x + 36 = 0$ (d) $x^2 + 20x + 5 = 0$
   (e) $x^2 + 8x - 9 = 0$ (f) $x^2 - 2x - 7 = 0$

3. Solve the following equations by completing the
   square. First write them in the form $x^2 + px + q = 0$.
   Leave square roots in your answers.
   (a) $2x^2 + 4x - 6 = 0$ (b) $3x^2 + 15x - 12 = 0$
   (c) $2x^2 + 10x + 1 = 0$ (d) $2x^2 + 8x - 12 = 0$

4. (a) If $f(x) = x^2 + 4x + 5$ then show that the equation
      can be written as $f(x) = (x + 2)^2 + 1$.
   (b) Use this to explain why $f(x)$ cannot take a value
      lower than 1.
   (c) Use this also to explain why $f(x)$ takes the
      minimum value of 1 when $x = -2$.

5. *Edible Reptiles* claims that its bags of snakes contain 5
   more snakes than the bags from *Snakes Alive* and that
   they charge 1 cent less per snake than *Snakes Alive*.
   Anjana buys a bag from *Snakes Alive* for $5.00. Dhruv
   buys a bag of the same snakes for $5.70 from *Edible
   Reptiles*.
   (a) If *n* is the number of snakes in a bag from *Snakes
      Alive* then find, in terms of *n*:
      (i) how many snakes are in a bag from *Edible
         Reptiles*
      (ii) the cost per snake (in cents) at both shops.
   (b) Set up an equation involving *n* and solve it to
      find *n*.

6. A rectangular box is 23 cm longer than it is wide. Its
   diagonal is 65 cm. If *x* is the width of the box then:
   (a) use Pythagoras' theorem to find an expression for
      the length of the box in terms of *x*
   (b) show that $x^2 + 23x - 1848 = 0$
   (c) solve this equation to find the exact value of *x*.

22 Solving inequalities

You can solve inequalities in the same way as you solve equations. You can:

*   add and subtract any number from both sides of an inequality
*   multiply and divide both sides of an inequality by a positive number.

If you multiply or divide by a negative number you have to reverse the inequality sign
e.g. $-3 < 1$ but $3 > -1$. Try to avoid doing this as it is easy to make a mistake.

Example

Solve $x + 2 > 7$.

$\quad x + 2 > 7$ Subtract 2 from both sides

$\qquad x > 5$

Example

Solve $3x > 18$.

$\quad 3x > 18$ Divide both sides by 3

$\quad x > 6$

Example

Solve $-7x > 21$.

$-7x > 21$	Add $7x$ to both sides	or $-7x > 21$	Divide by -7 and
$0 > 21 + 7x$	Subtract 21 from both sides		reverse inequality sign
$-21 > 7x$	Divide both sides by 7		
$-3 > x$			
$x < -3$		$x < -3$	This method is
			quicker but you can
			go wrong.

You can express inequalities on a number line.

$x > -3$ can be expressed as

$\qquad -3$

$x \leqslant 4$ can be expressed as

$\qquad\qquad\qquad 4$

$1 < x \leqslant 7$ can be expressed as

$\qquad 1 \qquad\qquad 7$

> How can you remember whether to fill in the circle or not?
>
> The signs $\geqslant$ and $\leqslant$ use more ink than $>$ and $<$.
>
> • uses more ink than ○
>
> "Less than or equal to" and "greater than or equal to" use more ink than "less than" or "greater than".
>
> $\leqslant$ goes with "less than or equal to" and •
> $\geqslant$ goes with "greater than or equal to" and •
>
> $<$ goes with "less than" and ○
> $>$ goes with "greater than" and ○

Exam question
CIE 0580 June '08 Paper 2 Q13

Solve the inequality $\dfrac{2x - 5}{8} > \dfrac{x + 4}{3}$

$\dfrac{2x - 5}{8} > \dfrac{x + 4}{3}$	Clear the fractions
$3(2x - 5) > 8(x + 4)$	Expand brackets
$6x - 15 > 8x + 32$	Simplify
$\qquad -2x > 47$	
$\qquad x < -23\frac{1}{2}$	

or $-2x > 47$	Add $2x$ to both sides
$0 > 47 + 2x$	Subtract 47
$-47 > 2x$	
$-23\frac{1}{2} > x$ or $x < -23\frac{1}{2}$	

Inequality sign flips because you divide both sides by -2

Using inequalities to describe regions

Solid and dotted and lines

Use solid lines to show that the points on the line are included in the region described by an inequality. So use solid lines for inequalities involving ⩽ or ⩾.

Use dotted lines to show that the points on the line are not included in the region described by an inequality. So use dotted lines for inequalities involving < or >.

> **How can you remember whether to use dotted line or solid lines?**
>
> The way to remember this is as before:
>
> The signs ⩾ and ⩽ use more ink than > and <.
>
> The solid line uses more ink than the dotted line so ⩾ and ⩽ go with solid lines.
> < and > go with dotted lines.

The line $y = 2x + 1$ splits the graph into two parts.

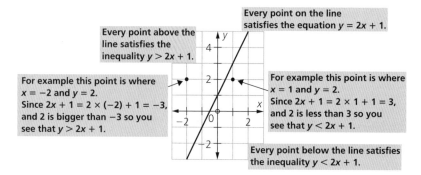

Every point above the line satisfies the inequality $y > 2x + 1$.

Every point on the line satisfies the equation $y = 2x + 1$.

For example this point is where $x = -2$ and $y = 2$.
Since $2x + 1 = 2 \times (-2) + 1 = -3$, and 2 is bigger than -3 so you see that $y > 2x + 1$.

For example this point is where $x = 1$ and $y = 2$.
Since $2x + 1 = 2 \times 1 + 1 = 3$, and 2 is less than 3 so you see that $y < 2x + 1$.

Every point below the line satisfies the inequality $y < 2x + 1$.

So $y < 2x + 1$ describes the region below the line $y = 2x + 1$. However you are often asked to shade the **unwanted** region so you would shade above the line.

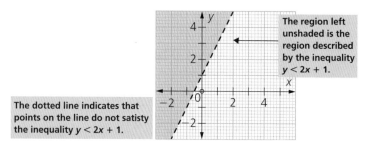

The region left unshaded is the region described by the inequality $y < 2x + 1$.

The dotted line indicates that points on the line do not satisfy the inequality $y < 2x + 1$.

Which area to shade?

- If you are asked to leave the region satisfied by the inequality $x > a$ **unshaded** then remember that:

  $x > a$ always describes the region to the right of $x = a$.
  So shade to the left of $x = a$.

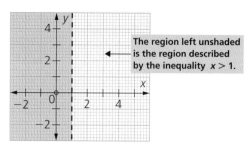

The region left unshaded is the region described by the inequality $x > 1$.

- $x < a$ always describes the region to the left of $x = a$.
  So shade to the right of $x = a$.

The region left unshaded is the region described by the inequality $x < 3$.

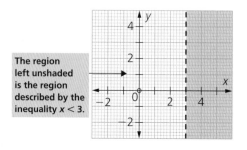

Extended

When dealing with inequalities of the form $ax + by > c$ or $ax + by < c$ you should always rearrange the equation (if necessary) so that b is positive.

- $ax + by > c$ (provided that $b > 0$) always describes the region **above** the line $ax + by = c$.
  So shade below the line $ax + by = c$.

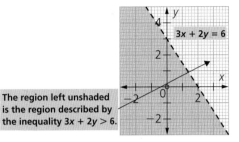

The region left unshaded is the region described by the inequality $3x + 2y > 6$.

- $ax + by < c$ (provided that $b > 0$) always describes the region **below** the line $ax + by = c$.
  So shade above the line $ax + by = c$.

The region left unshaded is the region described by the inequality $-4x + 3y < 12$.

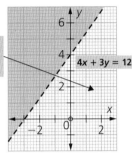

Example

By shading the unwanted region on the diagram, show the region defined by the inequalities $x \geqslant 2$, $y > 1$, $x + y < 6$

First draw the three lines $x = 2$, $y = 1$, $x + y = 6$

Use dotted lines for $x + y = 6$, $y = 1$ and a solid line for $x = 2$.

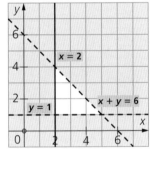

$x \geqslant 2$ describes the region to the right of $x = 2$.
So shade to the left of $x = 2$.
$y > 1$ describes the region above the line $y = 1$.
So shade below $y = 1$.
$x + y < 6$ describes the region below the line $x + y = 6$. So shade above $x + y = 6$.
The region $x \geqslant 2$, $y > 1$, $x + y < 6$ is shown unshaded.

Exam question   CIE 0580 June '06 Paper 2 Q20

(a) One of the lines in the diagram is labelled $y = mx + c$. Find the values of m and c.

(b) Show, by shading all the unwanted regions on the diagram, the region defined by the inequalities:

$$x \geqslant 1 \quad y \leqslant mx + c \quad y \geqslant x + 2 \quad \text{and} \quad y \geqslant 4$$

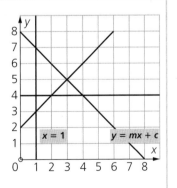

(a) As the line moves 1 unit to the right; it moves 1 unit down so the gradient of the line is -1.
So $m = -1$.
The y-intercept is 8. So $c = 8$.

(Continued)

Exam question (Continued)

(b) Use solid lines for all the lines as they all involve ⩽ or ⩾.

$x \geqslant 1$ describes the region to the right of $x = 1$ so shade to the left of $x = 1$.

$y \leqslant mx + c$ describes the region below $y = mx + c$ so shade above $y = mx + c$.

$y \geqslant x + 2$ describes the region above $y = x + 2$ so shade below $y = x + 2$

$y \geqslant 4$ describes the region above $y = 4$ so shade below $y = 4$.

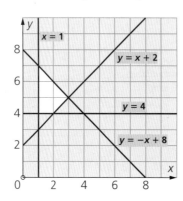

The unshaded region is defined by $x \geqslant 1$, $y \leqslant -x + 8$, $y \geqslant x + 2$, $y \geqslant 4$.

Questions

1. Leave unshaded the region defined by the following inequalities. Number both x- and y-axes from -8 to 8 with 1 cm per unit on each.
   (a) $y < 2x + 1$
   (b) $2y + x \leqslant 6$
   (c) $2x - 3y \leqslant 12$

2. Write down the inequalities which define the unshaded region shown below:

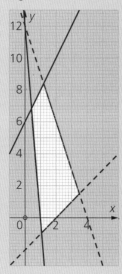

3. Leave unshaded the region defined by the following inequalities. Number the x-axis from -8 to 8 and the y-axis from -4 to 8 with 1 cm per unit on both axes.
   (a) $2x + 3y < 12$
   (b) $y - 2x \leqslant 4$
   (c) $x - 3y < 6$

4. Leave unshaded the region defined by the following inequalities. Number the x-axis from -8 to 8 and the y-axis from -4 to 8 with 1 cm per unit on both axes.
   (a) $y \leqslant 8 - 2x$
   (b) $4x - 3y > -24$
   (c) $4y - x \geqslant -4$
   (d) $6y + x > -6$

5. Leave unshaded the region defined by the following inequalities. Number both x- and y-axes from -6 to 6 with 1 cm per unit on each.
   (a) $3x + 2y \leqslant 12$
   (b) $3x - 2y \leqslant 12$
   (c) $3x - 2y \geqslant -12$
   (d) $3x + 2y \geqslant -12$

23 Linear programming

Linear programming is a graphical method of finding the best solution to a problem that is defined by simultaneous inequalities.

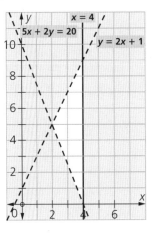

Example

(a) Leave unshaded the region defined by the inequalities $x \leqslant 4$, $y < 2x + 1$, $5x + 2y > 20$

(b) Find the maximum value of $x + y$ for points that have integer coordinates in this region.

(a) First draw the three lines $x = 4$, $y = 2x + 1$, $5x + 2y = 20$

Use dotted lines for $y = 2x + 1$ and $5x + 2y = 20$ and a solid line for $x = 4$.

Shade to the right of $x = 4$.
Shade above $y = 2x + 1$.
Shade below $5x + 2y = 20$

(b) In the unshaded region (the solution set) mark the points which have integer coordinates.
The possible points are marked as black dots on the diagram.

The table shows the value of $x + y$ at each of the possible points.

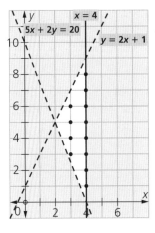

x	3	3	3	3	4	4	4	4	4	4	4	4
y	3	4	5	6	1	2	3	4	5	6	7	8
$x + y$	6	7	8	9	5	6	7	8	9	10	11	12

The maximum value of $x + y = 12$.

> Points on the dotted lines $y < 2x + 1$ and $5x + 2y > 20$ are not in the solution set.

Exam question

CIE 0580 November '06 Paper 4 Q9

Tiago does some work during the school holidays.
In one week he spends x hours cleaning cars and y hours repairing cycles.
The time he spends repairing cycles is at least equal to the time he spends cleaning cars.
This can be written as $y \geqslant x$.

He spends no more than 12 hours working.
He spends at least 4 hours cleaning cars.

   (a) Write down two more inequalities in x and/or y to show this information.
   (b) Draw x- and y-axes from 0 to 12, using a scale of 1 cm to represent 1 unit on each axis.
   (c) Draw three lines to show the three inequalities. Shade the unwanted regions.
   (d) Tiago receives $3 each hour for cleaning cars and $1.50 each hour for repairing cycles.
      (i) What is the least amount he could receive?
      (ii) What is the largest amount he could receive?

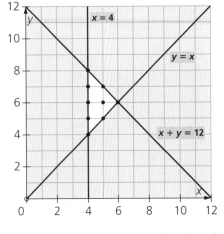

(a) He spends no more than 12 hours working means that $x + y \leqslant 12$
    He spends at least 4 hours cleaning cars means that $x \geqslant 4$
(b) see graph
(c) see graph
(d) Amount earned cleaning cars $\quad = 3x$
    Amount earned repairing cycles $= 1.5y$
    $\qquad\qquad$ Total earnings $= 3x + 1.5y$
    Find the minimum and maximum values of $3x + 1.5y$ for values

(Continued)

Extended

Exam question (Continued)

of x and y in the unshaded region.

The nine marked points on the graph represent possible solutions.

x	4	4	4	4	4	5	5	5	6
y	4	5	6	7	8	5	6	7	6
$3x + 1.5y$	18	19.5	21	22.5	24	22.5	24	25.5	27

(i) The least amount he could receive is $18.

(ii) The largest amount he could receive is $27.

Questions

1. Draw x- and y-axes from 0 to 10 using a scale of 1 cm to represent 1 unit on each axis.

(a) Leave unshaded the following region:

$x + y < 10$ $\qquad$ $y > 2x$ $\qquad$ $x \geqslant 1$

For integer values of x and y in this region find:

(b) the maximum value of $2y + x$

(c) the minimum value of $2y + x$.

2. Banu gets a gardening job in the school holidays. She rakes leaves for x hours and she weeds flower beds for y hours. Her employer tells her that she must spend at least as long weeding the flower beds as she spends raking the leaves. She is also told that she must spend at least 5 hours raking leaves but must spend less than 11 hours weeding the flower beds.

(a) Write down three inequalities for x and y.

(b) Draw x- and y-axes from 0 to 15 using a scale of 1 cm to represent 1 unit on each axis.

(c) Draw three lines to show the three inequalities and shade the **unwanted** regions.

Banu is paid $5 for each hour of raking leaves and $4 for each hour of weeding flower beds.

(d) Write down an expression for how much she earns when she rake leaves for x hours and weeds flower beds for y hours.

(e) (i) What is the least amount that she could receive?

(ii) What is the largest amount that she could receive?

3. A boy wants to buy a collection of books and magazines from a second-hand shop. The books cost $3 and the magazines cost $1. He has $20 to spend and the number of magazines he buys must be less than twice the number of books he buys. He wants to buy at least 8 items from the shop.

After reading the books and magazines he sells them on to friends at $5 for books and $2 for magazines. If he buys x books and y magazines:

(a) write down the three inequalities which describe the above situation

(b) draw a graph and show unshaded the region which is satisfied by these inequalities

(c) find the maximum amount he can make from selling these books and magazines to his friends.

24 Angles and polygons

Angles

One complete revolution is 360°.

So the angle at a point is 360°.

The angle on a line is 180°

Example

If a CD spins at 500 revolutions per minute then how many degrees does it turn through each second?

Each revolution is 360° so the CD spins through 360° × 500 = 180 000° per minute
= 180 000° ÷ 60 per second
= 3000° per second

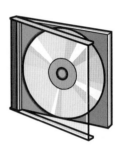

An **acute angle** is less than 90°.

An **obtuse angle** is between 90° and 180°.

A **reflex angle** is larger than 180° but less than 360°.

A **right angle** is 90°.

Example

Find the obtuse and reflex angles between the hands of a clock at 8 o'clock.

The obtuse angle = $\frac{1}{3}$ of 360° = 120°

The reflex angle = $\frac{2}{3}$ of 360° = 240°

Perpendicular lines

Perpendicular lines meet or intersect at right angles.
AB is perpendicular to *CD*.

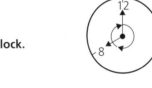

Intersecting lines

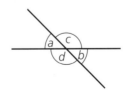

$a + b + c + d = 360°$ (angles at a point)
$a = b$ and $c = d$ (vertically opposite angles are equal)
$a + c = 180°$ and $b + d = 180°$ (angles on a straight line)

Parallel lines

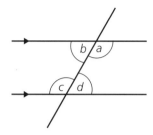 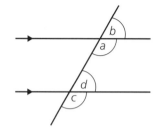

$a = c$ and $b = d$ (alternate angles)
$a + b = 180°$ and $c + d = 180°$
(angles on a straight line)

$a = c$ and $b = d$ (corresponding angles)
$c + d = 180°$ (angles on a straight line)
and so $a + d = 180°$ (since $a = c$)

Polygons

A polygon is a closed 2-dimensional shape with straight edges.

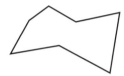 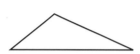

In a regular polygon all the sides are equal and all the angles are equal.

regular hexagon   square   equilateral triangle

A **triangle** is a three-sided polygon.
The three interior angles in a triangle add up to 180°.

$$a + b + c = 180°$$

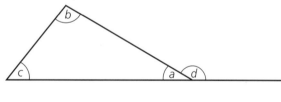

$$d = b + c$$

$a + b + c = 180°$ (angles in triangle)
$a + d = 180°$ (angles on a straight line)
It follows that $d = b + c$, or in words:
The exterior angle of a triangle
is equal to the sum of the two
interior opposite angles.

An **isosceles** triangle has two equal sides
and two equal angles.

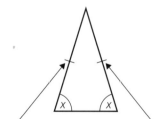

The marks indicate that the sides are equal.

An **equilateral** triangle has three
equal sides and three equal angles.

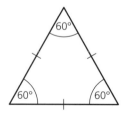

A **right-angled** triangle has one right angle.

A **quadrilateral** is a four-sided polygon. The sum of its interior angles is 360°.

Quadrilaterals with special features

Square
4 equal sides, 4 right angles

Rectangle
4 sides, 4 right angles, opposite sides equal

Parallelogram
4 sides, 2 sets of parallel sides,
opposite sides equal, opposite angles equal

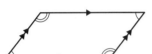

Rhombus
4 equal sides, opposite sides parallel,
opposite angles equal

Trapezium
4 sides, one set of opposite sides parallel

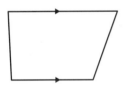

Kite
4 sides, 2 pairs of adjacent sides equal,
1 pair of opposite angles equal

Polygons with more than four sides

A **pentagon** has 5 sides.

The Pentagon in Washington

A **hexagon** has 6 sides.

Cells in a beehive

A **heptagon** has 7 sides

An **octagon** has 8 sides

Nets

If you cut along some of the edges of this cuboid and lay it out flat you have the **net**.
Cutting different edges gives different nets.

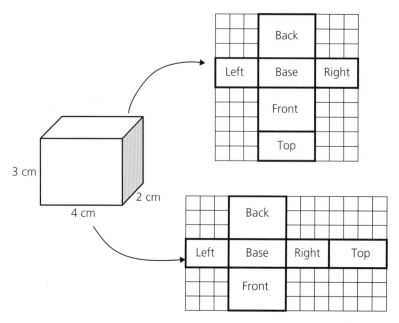

Interior and exterior angles

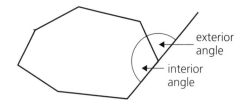

Sum of interior angles

An n-sided polygon can be split up into $(n - 2)$ triangles. The angles in each triangle add up
to 180° and so the angles in an n-sided polygon add up to $(n - 2) \times 180°$.

Example

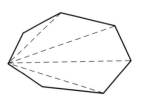

This 7-sided polygon can be split up into 5 triangles. So the angles in the 7-sided
polygon add up to $(7 - 2) \times 180° = 5 \times 180° = 900°$

Exterior angles

Imagine an ant standing at G and walking clockwise around the polygon.
It would turn through angle a when it got to A, b when it got to B etc.

By the time it got back to G it would have turned through 360°.

So $a + b + c + d + e + f + g = 360°$.

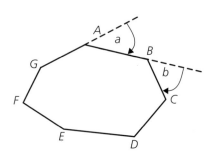

In a regular n-sided polygon the exterior angles are equal.

Each exterior angle $= \dfrac{360°}{n}$

- The sum of the exterior angles of any polygon (regular or irregular) is 360°.

Questions

1. Name these polygons.

(a)

(b)
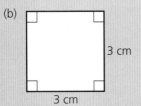

3 cm

3 cm

(c)

(d)
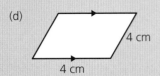

4 cm

4 cm

(e)

(f)
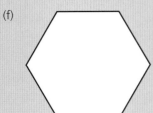

(g)
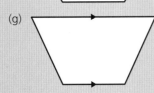

(h)

(i)
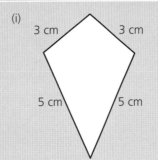

3 cm   3 cm

5 cm   5 cm

2. Find x in these quadrilaterals.

(a)
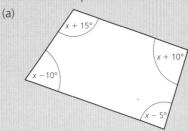

$x + 15°$

$x + 10°$

$x - 10°$

$x - 5°$

(b)
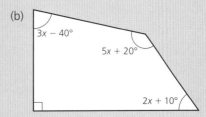

$3x - 40°$

$5x + 20°$

$2x + 10°$

3. Draw a sketch of a quadrilateral with:
(a) four sides
(b) four sides with two parallel sides
(c) four sides with two pairs of parallel sides
(d) four equal sides but no right angles
(e) four sides with two pairs of parallel sides and one pair of sides perpendicular to the other pair
(f) four sides with two pairs of adjacent sides equal

4. Name the quadrilaterals in question 3.

5. Find the sum of the interior angles of the polygons in question 1.

6. Name a polygon in which the sum of the interior angles is:
(a) 180°
(b) 540°
(c) 360°
(d) 720°

Extended

25 Circles

Angles in a circle

Angle in a semicircle

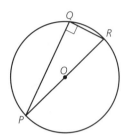

If *PR* is the diameter of a circle then ∠*PQR* is a right angle. This theorem is often stated as "the angle in a semicircle is a right angle" or "the angle subtended by the diameter is 90°".

Angle between radius and tangent

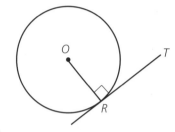

If *OR* is the radius of a circle and the line *RT* is a tangent to the circle at *R* then ∠*ORT* is a right angle. "The angle between the radius and the tangent is 90°".

Angle at centre

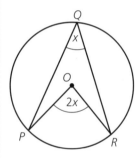

If *P*, *Q* and *R* are three points on a circle then the angle *POR* is twice the angle *PQR*.

"The angle at the centre is twice the angle at the circumference."

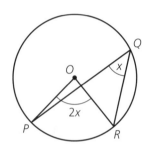

∠*POR* = 2 × ∠*PQR*

Angles in the same segment

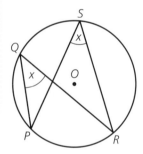

If *Q*, *P*, *R* and *S* are points on a circle with *Q* and *S* lying in the same segment then ∠*PQR* is equal to ∠*PSR*.

"Angles subtended by a chord or arc *PR* in the same segment are equal."

Example

Find *x* and *y*.

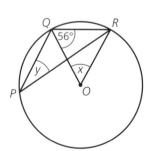

$OQ = OR$ (radii of the circle), so triangle *OQR* is isosceles

So ∠*QRO* = 56°.

$x + 56° + 56° = 180°$ (angles in a triangle)

so $x = 68°$

∠*QOR* = 2 × ∠*QPR* (angle at centre)

$68° = 2 × ∠QPR$

so $y = 34°$

Extended

Example

Find w, x, y and z.

$OP = OQ$ (radii), so triangle OPQ is isosceles
$$\text{so } w = 26°$$
$$x = 2 \times 26° = 52° \text{ (angle at centre)}$$
$$w + y = 90° \text{ angle in semicircle}$$
$$\text{so } y = 64°$$
$$z + 90° + 26° = 180° \text{ (angles in triangle)}$$
$$\text{so } z = 64°$$

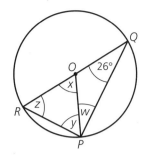

Alternatively, since triangle OPR is isosceles $z = y = 64°$

Opposite angle in cyclic quadrilateral

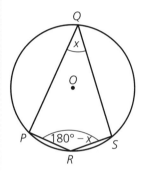

If Q, P, R and S are points on a circle with Q and R lying in different segments then the sum of $\angle PQS$ and $\angle PRS$ is 180°.

"The sum of opposite angles in a cyclic quadrilateral is 180°."

Example

Find x, y and z.

$$x = 42° \text{ (angles in same segment)}$$
$$y = 49° \text{ (angles in same segment)}$$
$$(y + 42°) + z = 180° \text{ (opposite angles of cyclic quadrilateral)}$$
$$\text{So } z = 180° - 42° - 49° = 89°$$

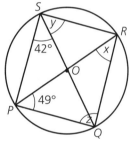

Exam question

CIE 0580 June '07 Paper 2 Q19

P, Q, R and S lie on a circle, centre O.
TP and TQ are tangents to the circle.
PR is a diameter and angle PSQ = 64°.

    (a) Work out the values of w and x.
    (b) Showing all your working, find the value of y.

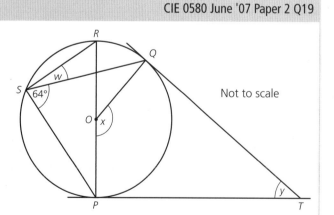

Not to scale

(a) $w + 64° = 90°$, so $w = 26°$ (angle in semicircle)
    $x = 2 \times 64° = 128°$ (angle at centre)

(b) $POQT$ is a quadrilateral so the sum of its interior angles is 360°.
    $\angle OPT = 90°$ and $\angle OQT = 90°$ (radius meeting tangent)
    $90° + 90° + 128° + y = 360°$
$$y = 360° - 90° - 90° - 128°$$
$$y = 52°$$

Extended

Exam question

CIE 0580 June '06 Paper 2 Q18

AD is a diameter of the circle *ABCDE*.
Angle *BAC* = 22° and angle *ADC* = 60°.
AB and *ED* are parallel lines.
Find the values of *w*, *x*, *y* and *z*.

$\angle ACD = 90°$ (angle in semicircle)
$w + 60° + 90° = 180°$ (angles in triangle)
So $w = 30°$
$x = 22°$ (angle in same segment)
$y = w = 30°$ (angle in same segment)
$\angle ABE = \angle BED = x + y = 52°$ (*AB* ∥ *ED*, alternate angles)
$z = \angle ABE = 52°$ (angle in same segment)

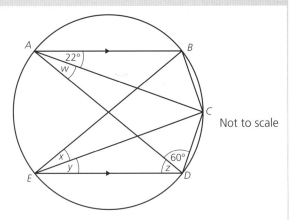

Not to scale

Questions

In questions 1–12, find, giving reasons, the angles shown by letters. The only circle laws which may be used are "angle at centre" and "angles in same segment". In addition "isosceles triangle", "angles at a point/on a line" etc. can be given as reasons. In each circle, *O* is the centre.

1.

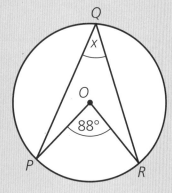

2.

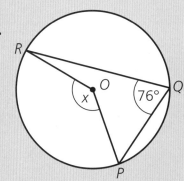

3.

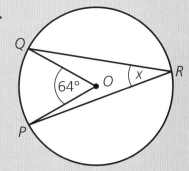

4.

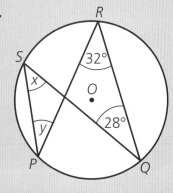

5.

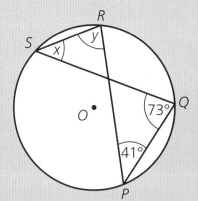

6.

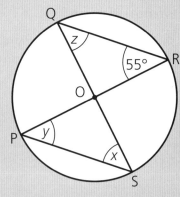

7.

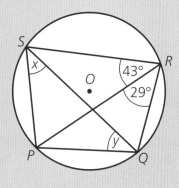

8.

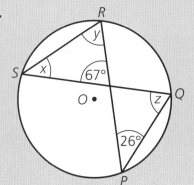

9.

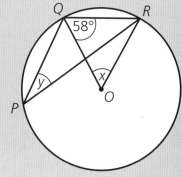

Questions

10.
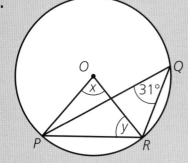

11.
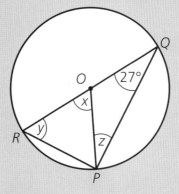

12.
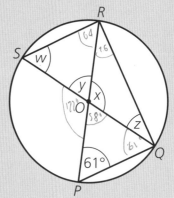

In questions 13–21, find, giving reasons, the angles shown by letters. The only circle laws which may be used are "angle at centre", "angles in same segment" and "opposite angles in cyclic quadrilateral". In addition "isosceles triangle", "angles at a point/on a line" etc. can be given as reasons. In each circle, O is the centre.

13.
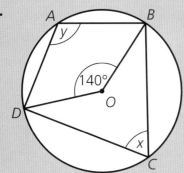

14.
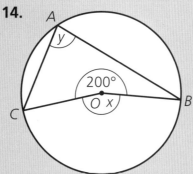

15.
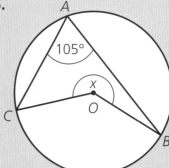

16.
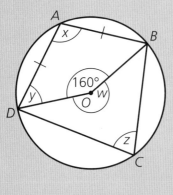

17.
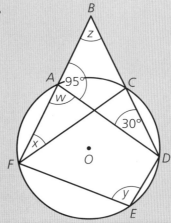

18.
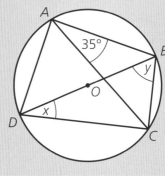

19.
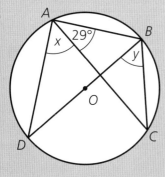

20.
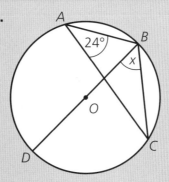

21.
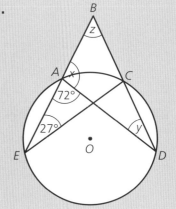

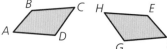

26 Similar shapes

Congruent shapes

Two shapes are **congruent** if the corresponding angles and the corresponding sides are equal.

These two quadrilaterals are congruent.

$AB = EF$, $BC = EH$, $CD = GH$ and $AD = FG$

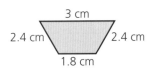

Similar shapes

Two shapes are **similar** (or mathematically similar) if the ratio of every pair of corresponding sides is the same. That is to say one of the shapes is an enlargement of the other.

Example

Are these two shapes mathematically similar?

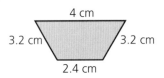

The ratios of the corresponding sides are $\frac{1.8}{2.4}$, $\frac{3}{4}$, $\frac{2.4}{3.2}$ and $\frac{2.4}{3.2}$. All these ratios are equal to 0.75 so the two shapes are similar.

Example

Find x given that these two shapes are similar.

Ratios of corresponding sides are equal,

so $\frac{x}{6} = \frac{7}{4}$

$x = \frac{42}{4} = 10.5$ cm

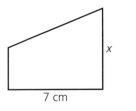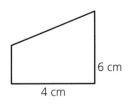

Example

Find x and y in triangle ABC.

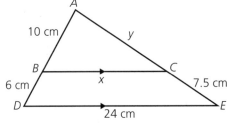

Draw the two similar triangles separately and mark on all the lengths.

Triangles ABC and ADE are similar,

so $\frac{x}{24} = \frac{10}{16}$

$x = 15$ cm

and $\frac{y + 7.5}{y} = \frac{16}{10}$ (Crossmultiply)

$10(y + 7.5) = 16y$

$10y + 75 = 16y$

$6y = 75$

$y = 12.5$ cm

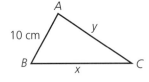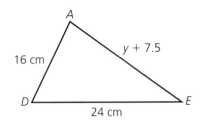

Similar areas and volumes

Area

If two shapes are similar then the ratio of their areas is equal to the **square** of the ratio of their sides.

Example

Two triangles are similar. Their bases are 5 cm and 8 cm. The area of the smaller triangle is 24 cm². Find the area of the larger triangle.

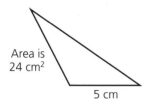 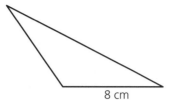

Area is
24 cm²   5 cm   8 cm

So if area of the larger triangle is A then $\dfrac{A}{24} = \left(\dfrac{8}{5}\right)^2$

Hence $A = 24 \times \left(\dfrac{8}{5}\right)^2 = 61.44 \text{ cm}^2$

> This is easy to remember because units of top and bottom of the left-hand side are cm² so square the right-hand side to get the same units.

Example

Find the area of a lake on a 1:20 000 map given that the area of the lake is 20 cm² on the map.

If true area of lake is A,

$\dfrac{A}{20} = \left(\dfrac{20\,000}{1}\right)^2$ and so $A = 20 \times \left(\dfrac{20\,000}{1}\right)^2 = 8\,000\,000\,000 \text{ cm}^2 = 0.8 \text{ km}^2$

Another method is to imagine the lake as a rectangle measuring 1 cm by 20 cm on the map.
1 cm on the map is 20 000 cm = 200 m = 0.2 km on the ground
20 cm on the map is 400 000 cm = 4000 m = 4 km on the ground
So actual area of lake is 0.2 km × 4 km = 0.8 km²

> It is often easier to consider the shape as a rectangle and make up dimensions for the width and length that give the required area.

Exam question   CIE 0580 June '07 Paper 4 Q1 a

The scale of a map is 1:20 000 000.
On the map, the distance between Cairo and Addis Ababa is 12 cm.
   (a) Calculate the distance, in kilometres, between Cairo and Addis Ababa.
   (b) On the map the area of a desert region is 13 square centimetres.
       Calculate the actual area of this desert region, in square kilometres.

(a) 12 cm on the map represents 12 × 20 000 000 = 240 000 000 cm on the
     ground
     240 000 000 cm = 2 400 000 m = 2400 km
(b) Consider the desert as measuring 1 cm by 13 cm
     If 12 cm represents 2400 km then 1 cm represents 200 km and
     13 cm represents 2600 km.
     So area of desert is 200 km × 2600 km = 520 000 km²

Extended

Volume

If two shapes are similar then the ratio of their volumes is equal to the **cube** of the ratio of their sides.

Example

Two similar bottles have radius 3 cm and 5 cm respectively. If the volume of the smaller bottle is 54 cm³, what is the volume of the larger one?

If V is the volume of the larger bottle, $\dfrac{V}{54} = \left(\dfrac{5}{3}\right)^3$

Hence $V = 54 \times \left(\dfrac{5}{3}\right)^3 = 250$ cm³

> This is easy to remember because units of top and bottom of the left-hand side are cm³ so cube the right-hand side to get the same units.

Finding a side when one side and two areas or two volumes are given

Example

Two bottles are similar; one has volume of 1200 cm³ and the other has volume 1900 cm³. If the height of the smaller bottle is 10 cm find the height of the larger bottle.

$$\left(\dfrac{h}{10}\right)^3 = \dfrac{1900}{1200}$$

Take cube root of both sides: $\dfrac{h}{10} = \sqrt[3]{\dfrac{1900}{1200}}$ and so $h = 10 \times \sqrt[3]{\dfrac{19}{12}} = 11.7$ cm (to 3 sf)

Example

Two containers are similar. One has a volume of 8000 cm³ and a surface area of 5000 cm². The other has a volume of 4000 cm³ and surface area A. Find A.

Ratio of volumes $= \dfrac{4000}{8000}$

Ratio of sides $= \sqrt[3]{\dfrac{4000}{8000}} = \sqrt[3]{0.5}$

So $\dfrac{A}{5000} = \left(\sqrt[3]{0.5}\right)^2$

$A = 5000 \times \left(\sqrt[3]{0.5}\right)^2$

$= 3150$ cm² (to 3 sf)

Exam question

CIE 0580 November '06 Paper 2 Q13 a

A statue two metres high has a volume of five cubic metres.
A similar model of the statue has a height of four centimetres.
Calculate the volume of the model statue in cubic centimetres.

Let the volume of the model be V.
$1 \text{ m}^3 = 1 \text{ m} \times 1 \text{ m} \times 1 \text{ m} = 100 \text{ cm} \times 100 \text{ cm} \times 100 \text{ cm} = 1\,000\,000 \text{ cm}^3$

So volume of statue $= 5\,000\,000$ cm³

Ratio of volumes $= \dfrac{V}{5\,000\,000}$

Ratio of heights $= \dfrac{4}{200}$

$\dfrac{V}{5\,000\,000} = \left(\dfrac{4}{200}\right)^3$ so $V = 5\,000\,000 \times \left(\dfrac{4}{200}\right)^3 = 40$ cm³

The volume of the model is 40 cm³.

> It is easier to calculate if the smaller volume (in this example V) is in the numerator.

Questions

1. Ben and Sarah want to measure the height of a building. Ben is 1.8 m tall and Sarah suggests that he stands next to the building and compares the shadows. She measures his shadow to be 2.4 m long and the shadow of the building to be 16 m long. How tall is the building?

2. A photocopier is set to reduce the lengths of copies to $\frac{2}{3}$ of the original size. If the original document measures 12 cm by 15 cm what will be the dimensions of the copy?

3. A photography shop produces enlargements of photos. A 15 cm × 10 cm photo was enlarged so that its longest side was 24 cm. What was the length of the shorter side?

4. A map is reduced to $\frac{3}{5}$ of its original size. A field on the original map measured 25 mm × 35 mm. What will be its dimensions on the image?

5. A map that measures 24 cm by 30 cm is reduced to $\frac{2}{3}$ of its original size. What are the dimensions of the reduced map?

6. In the triangle in the diagram $BD = 8$ cm, $AB = 10$ cm, $AD = 6$ cm, $AC = x$ and $CD = y$.
   (a) Draw the two triangles ABC and DBA in the same orientation and mark on all their angles.
   (b) Hence explain why triangles ABC and DBA are similar.
   (c) Write down an equation involving x.
   (d) Solve the equation to find x.
   (e) Calculate the value of y.

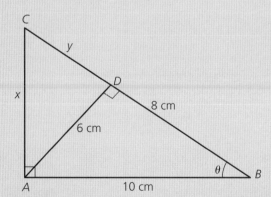

7. A rectangle P is enlarged to a rectangle Q. The dimensions of P are 5 m by 12 m. The shortest side of Q is 6 m.
   (a) What is the scale factor of enlargement?
   (b) What is the length of the longer side of Q?

8. A right-angled triangle P is enlarged to a triangle Q. The hypotenuse of P is 12 cm and the hypotenuse of Q is 15 cm.
   (a) What is the scale factor of enlargement?
   (b) If the shortest side of P is 8 cm find the shortest side of Q.

9. A photo 8 cm high and 10 cm wide has a border 2 cm high along the bottom and the top of the photo and w cm wide on each side. Find w if the original photo is similar to the photo with its border.

10.

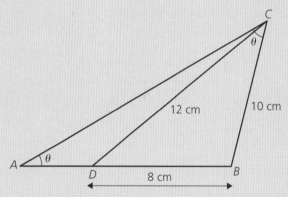

   In the diagram $\angle DCB = \angle CAB = \theta$, $DB = 8$ cm, $DC = 12$ cm and $CB = 10$ cm.
   (a) To which triangle is triangle ABC similar?
   (b) Draw triangle ABC and the triangle of part (a) so that they have the same orientation and mark each side clearly.
   (c) Find the length AB.
   (d) Find also the length AC.

11. A cone of radius 6 cm and height 15 cm has a cone of height 9 cm removed from its top. What is the radius of the removed cone?

12. The distance between Delhi and Calcutta is 1310 km. On a map they are 26.2 cm apart. Find the scale of the map in the form $1:n$.

13. The scale of a map is $1:20\,000\,000$. On the map the area of a state is 5 cm². Calculate the actual area of the state in km².

Extended

Questions (Continued)

14. In the diagram $AB = 5$ cm, $BC = 4$ cm and the area of the triangle ABE is 23 cm^2. Given that BE is parallel to CD find (to 2 sf) the area of the triangle ACD.

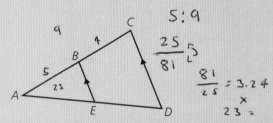

S : 9

$\dfrac{25}{81}$

$\dfrac{81}{25} = 3.24$
× 23 =

A = 74.5

15. Two large water tanks are similar. One holds 5 m^3 and the other holds 12 m^3. If the height of the smaller one is 1.2 m what is the height (to 3 sf) of the larger one?

16. Two pictures are similar. The area of one is 54 cm^2 and of the other is 216 cm^2. If the length of the larger one is 18 cm find the length of the smaller one.

17. Three layers of wedding cake are similar. The middle layer has a surface area of 3600 cm^2 and a mass of 5 kg.
 (a) What is the mass (to 3 sf) of the bottom layer if its surface area is 8000 cm^2?
 (b) What is the surface area (to 3 sf) of the top layer if its mass is 3 kg?

18. Two cuboids are similar. One has volume 6 m^3 and the other has volume 11 m^3. If the surface area of the smaller one is 22 m^2 what is the surface area (to 3 sf) of the larger one?

27 Geometrical constructions

Constructing a triangle

This example shows you how to construct, that is, make an accurate drawing of, a triangle using only a ruler and a pair of compasses.

Example

Construct a triangle of lengths 5 cm, 6 cm and 8 cm using only a ruler and compasses.

1. Draw a straight line about 10 cm long and mark a point A at one end.

2. With centre A and radius 8 cm mark a point B on the line.
   (To do this adjust the compasses to 8 cm and put the compass point on A.)

3. With centre A and radius 5 cm draw an arc above AB.

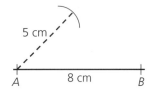

4. With centre B and radius 6 cm draw an arc to cut the first arc at C.

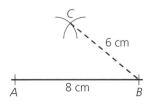

5. Join AC and BC.

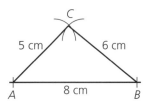

Constructing an angle bisector

Example

Construct the line which bisects the angle BAC using only a ruler and compasses.

1. With centre A draw an arc to cut AB at X.

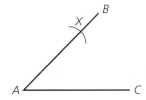

2. With the **same radius** draw an arc to cut AC at Y.

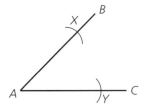

3. With centre X draw an arc to the right of B and C.

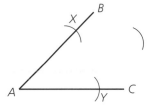

4. With the **same radius** and centre Y draw an arc to cut the previous arc at D.
5. Join AD.

   AD is the bisector of ∠BAC.

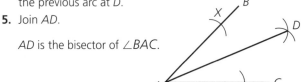

Constructing the perpendicular bisector of a straight line

The perpendicular bisector of a straight line *AB* is the line which cuts *AB* into two equal parts and crosses *AB* at right angles.

Example

Construct the perpendicular bisector of *AB* using only a ruler and compasses.

1. With centre *A* and radius greater than half *AB* draw arcs above and below *AB*.

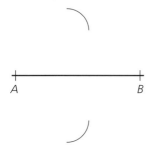

2. With the same radius and centre *B* draw arcs to cut the previous arcs at *X* and *Y*.

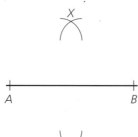

3. Join *XY*.

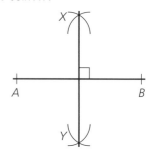

XY is the perpendicular bisector of *AB*.

Questions

1. Construct an equilateral triangle *ABC* where *AB* is
   (a) 5 cm
   (b) 3.7 cm

2. (a) Construct a line which passes through *A* and which makes an angle of 60° to *A*.

   (b) Bisect this angle to construct an angle of 30°.

3. Construct a triangle *ABC* in which the angle *ABC* is a right angle and the angle *BAC* is 60°.

4.

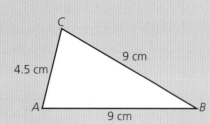

   (a) Make a full-size copy of the diagram. Find the midpoint of *AB*. Label this point *D*.
   (b) Find the midpoint of *AC*. Label this point *E*.
   (c) Find the midpoint of *BC*. Label this point *F*.
   (d) Draw the lines *CD*, *BE* and *AF*.
   (e) What do you notice about these three lines?

5.

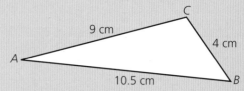

   (a) Make a full-size copy of the diagram. Use a set square to draw a line perpendicular to *AB* which passes through *C*.
   (b) Label the point where this line intersects *AB* as the point *D*.
   (c) Find the midpoint of *AC* by construction and label it *X*.
   (d) Draw a circle with centre *X* which passes through *A*.
   (e) What other points does your circle pass through?

28 Symmetry

Line symmetry

The dotted lines show the lines of symmetry for some letters.

An equilateral triangle has three lines of symmetry.

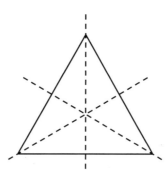

A square has four lines of symmetry.

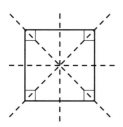

A rectangle has two lines of symmetry.

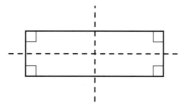

A parallelogram has no lines of symmetry.

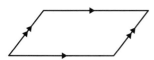

A rhombus has two lines of symmetry.

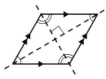

A trapezium has no line of symmetry.

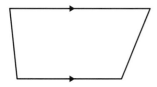

A kite has one line of symmetry.

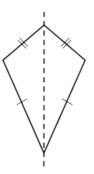

A regular *n*-sided polygon has *n* lines of symmetry.

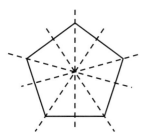

A regular pentagon has five lines of symmetry.

Rotational symmetry

 If you rotate the S through 360° about the marked point it will have two identical positions. The S has rotational symmetry of order 2.

 If you rotate this equilateral triangle through 360° about its centre it will have three identical positions. An equilateral triangle has rotational symmetry of order 3.

A square has rotational symmetry of order 4.

A rectangle has rotational symmetry of order 2.

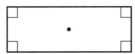

A parallelogram has rotational symmetry of order 2.

A rhombus has rotational symmetry of order 2.

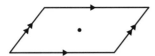

A trapezium has rotational symmetry of order 1.

A kite has rotational symmetry of order 1.

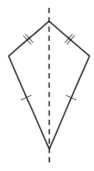

Notice that all shapes have rotational symmetry of order at least 1.

A regular n-sided polygon has order of rotational symmetry n.

In summary:

Polygon	Lines of symmetry	Order of rotational symmetry
Isosceles triangle	1	1
Equilateral Triangle	3	3
Square	4	4
Rectangle	2	2
Parallelogram	0	2
Rhombus	2	2
Kite	1	1
Trapezium	0	1
Regular n-sided polygon	n	n

Example

For these shapes
(a) draw all the lines of symmetry
(b) state the order of rotational symmetry.

(i) 　　(ii) 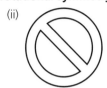　　(iii)

(a) the lines of symmetry

(i) 　　(ii) 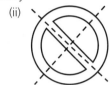　　(iii)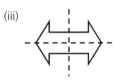

(b) the order of rotational symmetry.

(i) 　　(ii) 　　(iii)

Order 1　　　　　Order 2　　　　　　Order 2

Example

Write down
(a) the number of lines of symmetry
(b) the order of rotational symmetry of these shapes.

(i) 　　　　　　　(ii)

(a) Lines of symmetry

(i) 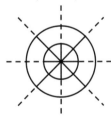　　　　　(ii)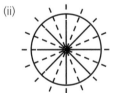

　　　　　　　　　　　　　　8 lines of symmetry

4 lines of symmetry

(b) Order of rotational of symmetry

(i) When is rotated by 45° the result is (which is different).

Rotating by 90°, 180°, 270° and 360° gives the same shape.

So the order of rotational symmetry is 4.

(ii) This shape has rotational symmetry of order 8.

Symmetry properties of circles
Equal chords

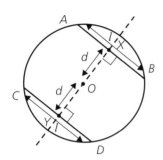

If two chords *AB* and *CD* have equal length then they are the same perpendicular distance from the centre of the circle.

OX = OY

Bisector of chord

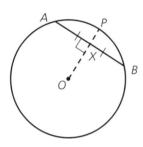

The perpendicular line from the centre of a circle to a chord bisects the chord.

AX = XB

Tangents

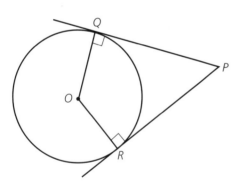

The tangents from a point *P* outside a circle to two points *Q* and *R* on the circle are equal in length.

PQ = PR

Solids
Rotational symmetry

The cylinder and the cone both have an axis of symmetry.

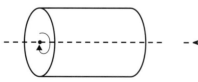 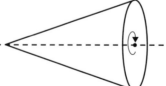

A prism whose cross-section is a regular *n*-sided polygon has order of rotational symmetry *n*.

For example, a pentagonal prism has rotational symmetry of order 5.

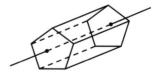

Extended

Planes of symmetry

A cuboid has three planes of symmetry.

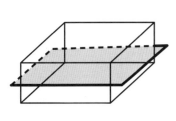 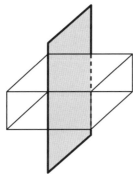 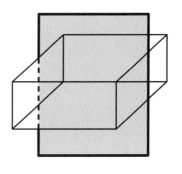

A prism whose cross-section is a regular *n*-sided polygon has *n* + 1 planes of symmetry.
For example, a pentagonal prism has 6 planes of symmetry.

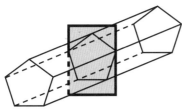 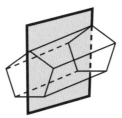

One plane like this   5 planes like this

Exam question   CIE 0580 June '06 Paper 2 Q21

(a) Shade one square in each diagram so that there is:

(i) one line of symmetry   **(ii) rotational symmetry of order 2.**

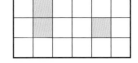   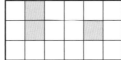

(b) On the diagram below, sketch one of the three planes of symmetry of the cuboid.

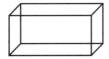

(c) Write down the order of rotational symmetry of the equilateral triangular prism about the axis shown.

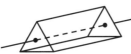

(a) (i)   (ii) rotational symmetry of order 2

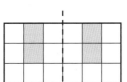   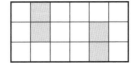

(b)

(c)   The order of rotational symmetry is 3 since as the prism is rotated there are
      three identical positions.

Questions

1. Copy the following shapes and
  (a) draw on all the lines of symmetry
  (b) state the order of rotational symmetry.

(i) $ (ii) ∩   (iii) ⊖   (iv) ✝

(v) 8   (vi) B   (vii) T   (viii) M

2. For this shape write down:
  (a) the order of rotational symmetry

  (b) the number of lines of symmetry.

3. Draw axes with values of x and y from −10 to 10.
Draw the shapes and fill in the table.

	Shape	Vertices	Missing vertices	Lines of symmetry
(a)	Rectangle	(1, 1), (5, 1), (5, 3)	(__,__)	$x = 3$, $y =$ __
(b)	Rectangle	(6, 1), (6, 9)	(__,__) (__,__)	$x = 8$, $y = 5$
(c)	Isosceles triangle	(3, 5), (5, 5), (4, 9)		$x =$ __
(d)	Isosceles triangle	(0, 5), (3, 7)	(__,__)	$y = 7$ only
(e)	Rhombus	(−3, 0), (−1, 1), (0, 3)	(__,__)	$y = -x$, $y =$ __
(f)	Trapezium	(3, −4), (2, −7), (7, −7)	(__,__)	$x = 4.5$ only
(g)	Parallelogram	(−6, −6), (−5, −3), (−2, −3)	(__,__)	None
(h)	Square	(−7, 3), (−5, −3)	(__,__)	$y = x + 8$ $x =$ __ $y =$ __ $y =$ __

4. (a) Shade one square in each diagram so that there is:
  (i) one line of symmetry

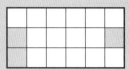

  (ii) rotational symmetry of order 2

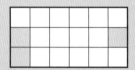

(b) The cuboid shown below has no square faces.
How many planes of symmetry does it have?

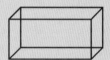

(c) How many planes of symmetry has a regular hexagonal prism?

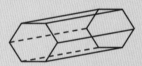

(d) Write down the order of rotational symmetry of the regular hexagonal prism about the axis shown.

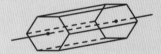

29 Locus

The locus of a point is the path traced out as it moves.

Some important loci

The plural of locus is "loci".

1. The locus of points which are a fixed distance d from a given point is a circle. The radius of the circle is d.

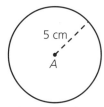

locus of points
5 cm from A

2. The locus of points which are **less** than a fixed distance from a given point is the region **inside** a circle.

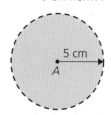

locus of points less than
5 cm from A

3. The locus of points more than a certain distance from a given point is the region **outside** a circle.

4. (a) The locus of points which are a fixed distance from a given straight line is a pair of parallel lines.

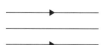

   (b) The locus of points a fixed distance from a line segment is shown in this diagram.

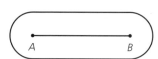

5. The locus of points which are equidistant from two fixed points A and B is the perpendicular bisector of AB.

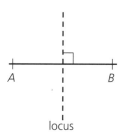

6. The locus of points which are closer to point A than point B is shown in the diagram.

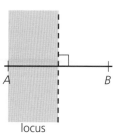

7. The locus of points which are equidistant from two fixed lines AB and AC is the angle bisector of angle BAC.

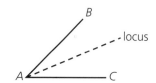

Sometimes a locus consists of the intersection of two loci as in the next example.

Example

Find the points which are 2 cm from *A* and 3 cm from *B*.
   With centre *A* and radius 2 cm draw two arcs. Repeat with
   centre *B* and radius 3 cm. The points *X* and *Y* at the intersection
   of the arcs are 2 cm from *A* and 3 from *B*.

A   *B*

Questions

4 / 4

1. Sketch the following loci. Describe each locus in
   words.
   (a) The locus of a point *P* which moves so that it is
       always 4 cm from a fixed point *A*.
   (b) The locus of a point *R* which moves so that it is
       always 2 cm from a line *AB*, 5 cm long.
   (c) The locus of a point *P* which is equidistant from
       two points *C* and *D*, 6 cm apart.
   (d) The locus of a point *S* equidistant from two lines
       AB and *AC* which meet at right angles at *A*.

2. Draw a pair of axes with *x* and *y* ranging from -3 to 3
   (use 2 cm per unit on both axes).
   (a) Draw the locus of a point which is 2 units away
       from the point *A* (1, 1)
   (b) Draw the locus of a point which is the same
       distance from *B*(-2, 1) as from *C* (1, -3)
   (c) Shade the locus of all points which are closer to *C*
       than to *B* and less than 2 units away from *A*.

3. A shed of dimensions 7 m by 3 m is in the middle of
   a large field of grass. A goat is tethered by a rope 5 m
   long to a corner of the shed.
   (a) Using a scale of 1 cm for 1 m, draw an accurate
       diagram of the shed and the area of grass the goat
       is able to eat.
   (b) Calculate this area (to 3 sf).

4. (a) Using a scale of 1 cm for 10 m, draw a diagram of
       a rectangular field 100 m by 60 m and mark the
       midpoint *A* of this field, where there is a tree.
   (b) A boy flies a kite in the field and doesn't want to
       stand closer than 20 m to the tree or closer than
       10 m to the low wall which surrounds the field.
       (i) Shade the region in which the boy can stand.
       (ii) Showing all your working clearly, find the area
            (to 3 sf) in which the boy can stand.

(c) A farmer wants to erect a fence so that no one
   can get closer than 10 m to any part of his field.
   (i) On your diagram mark this fence.
   (ii) Showing all your working clearly, find the
        perimeter (to 3 sf) of the fence.

5. A ladder of length 2 m leans against a vertical
   wall so that the ladder itself is in an almost vertical
   position. The foot of the ladder is on the horizontal
   floor. The ladder slips down the wall in such a way
   that the top of the ladder remains in contact with
   the wall and the foot of the ladder remains in
   contact with the floor.
   (a) Draw a diagram of the wall and floor and draw
       on it five positions which the ladder takes as it
       slides down to the floor. Use a scale of 1 cm
       for 20 cm.
   (b) Mark the midpoint, *M*, of the ladder on each of
       these positions.
   (c) What is the locus of the point *M*?

6. A ball with diameter 10 cm rolls down the steps
   shown in the diagram.

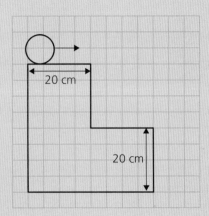

Sketch the locus of the centre of the ball.

30 Mensuration

Length

10 mm = 1 cm
100 cm = 1 m
1000 m = 1 kilometre

Area

So 1 cm^2 = 10 mm × 10 mm = 100 mm^2

In the same way:
1 m^2 = 100 cm × 100 cm = 10 000 cm^2

1 km^2 = 1000 m × 1000 m = 1 000 000 m^2

Example

How many square centimetres are there in 5 square metres?

Imagine a shape with area 5 m^2. The simplest shape is a rectangle measuring 1 m by 5 m.

Area = 1 × 5 m^2
= 100 × 500 cm^2
= 50 000 cm^2

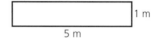

There are 50 000 square centimetres in 5 square metres.

Area and perimeter formulae

Rectangle

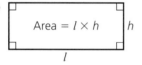

Perimeter = 2l + 2h

Triangle

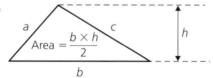

Perimeter = $a + b + c$

Example

Find the areas of these triangles.

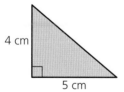

Area $= \frac{1}{2}$ × base × height
$= \frac{1}{2}$ × 5 × 4
= 10 cm^2

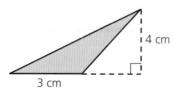

Area $= \frac{1}{2}$ × base × height
$= \frac{1}{2}$ × 3 × 4
= 6 cm^2

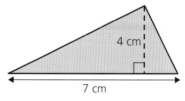

Area $= \frac{1}{2}$ × base × height
$= \frac{1}{2}$ × 7 × 4
= 14 cm^2

Parallelogram

The area of the parallelogram is the same as the area of the dotted rectangle.

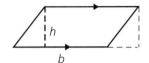

So area of parallelogram = $b \times h$, that is base × height

Trapezium

The area of the trapezium is the same as the area of the two dotted rectangles.

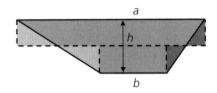

So area of trapezium = $a \times \frac{h}{2} + b \times \frac{h}{2}$

$\qquad\qquad\qquad = \frac{1}{2}(a + b) \times h$

that is, half the sum of parallel sides × height

Circle

Area of circle = πr^2
Circumference of circle = $2\pi r$

> Find out how to get π on your calculator.

Extended

Sector of circle

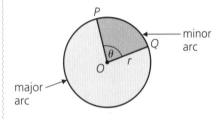

Length of minor arc = $\frac{\theta}{360} \times 2\pi r$

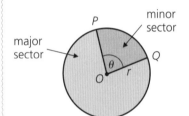

Area of minor sector = $\frac{\theta}{360} \times \pi r^2$

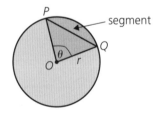

Area of segment
= (Area of minor sector) − (Area of triangle OPQ)

Example
Find the area of this shape.

Area of rectangle = $4 \times 10 = 40$ cm^2

Area of triangle = $\dfrac{4 \times 6}{2} = 12$ cm^2

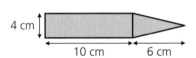

Area of whole shape = $40 + 12 = 52$ cm^2

Example

A birthday cake has radius 12 cm. A piece in the shape of a sector of angle 40° is cut from the cake.

(a) What is the cross-sectional area of the top of this piece of cake?

(b) What is the total perimeter of the top of this piece of cake?

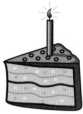

(a) The top of the birthday cake is a sector.

Area of sector $= \frac{40}{360} \times \pi \times 12^2 = \frac{40}{360} \times 144\pi$

$= 16\pi = 50.3 \text{ cm}^2$ (to 3 sf)

(b) Length of arc $= \frac{40}{360} \times 2 \times \pi \times 12 = \frac{8}{3}\pi$

$= 8.38 \text{ cm}$ (to 3 sf)

Perimeter = arc length + 2 radii

So total perimeter $= 8.38 + 12 + 12 = 32.4 \text{ cm}$ (to 3 sf)

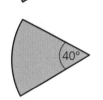

```
                              M   Math ▲
  40
 ─── ×π×12²
 360
            50.26548246
```

```
                              M   Math ▲
  40
 ─── ×2×π×12
 360
             8.37758041
```

Example

Find the area of this segment.

Area of minor sector $= \frac{67}{360} \times \pi \times 8^2 = 37.419859... \text{ cm}^2$

Area of triangle $OAB = \frac{1}{2} \times 8 \times 8 \times \sin 67° = 29.456155... \text{ cm}^2$

See Chapter 31 for area of triangle

So area of segment

= (area of minor sector) − (area of triangle OAB)

$= 37.419859 - 29.456155$

$= 7.96 \text{ cm}^2$ to 3 sf

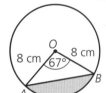

Volume and surface area

So 1 cm³ = 10 mm × 10 mm × 10 mm = 1000 mm³

Remember that 1 litre is 1000 cm³ and that 1 tonne = 1000 kg

Prism

A 3-dimensional shape which has the same cross-section throughout is called a prism.

The volume of a prism = cross-sectional area × height.

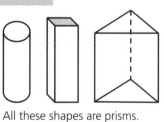

All these shapes are prisms.

Cylinder

A cylinder is a prism whose cross-section is a circle.

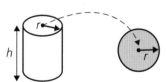

Cross-sectional area $= \pi r^2$
Volume of cylinder $= \pi r^2 h$

Volume of cylinder = cross-sectional area × height $= \pi r^2 \times h$

The surface area of a cylinder is made up of three parts: the curved surface, the top and the base.

For example a tin of sweetcorn is a cylinder.

The top. This is a circle with area πr^2.

The curved surface. If the label is peeled off it forms a rectangle of width $2\pi r$ (the circumference of the base) and height h. So its area is $2\pi rh$.

The base. This is a circle with area πr^2.

$$\text{Surface area of cylinder} = 2\pi r^2 + 2\pi rh$$
$$= 2\pi r(r + h)$$

Cuboid

A cuboid is a prism whose cross-section is a rectangle

Volume of cuboid = cross-sectional area × height
$$= b \times l \times h$$

A cuboid has six faces.
The front and back faces have area $h \times l$
The left and right faces have area $h \times b$
Top and bottom faces have area $b \times l$
Surface area of cuboid = $2hl + 2hb + 2bl$

Pyramid

A pyramid is a solid with a polygon for a base. All the other faces are triangles which meet at a common point.

Triangular pyramid or tetrahedron   Square-based pyramid

Volume of pyramid = $\frac{1}{3} \times$ (base area) × height.

Cone

A cone is a pyramid with a circular base.

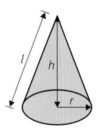

Volume of cone = $\frac{1}{3} \times$ (base area) × height
$$= \frac{1}{3} \times \pi r^2 \times h$$
$$= \frac{1}{3}\pi r^2 h$$

Curved surface area of cone = $\pi l r$ where l is the slant height.

Extended

Sphere

Volume of sphere $= \frac{4}{3}\pi r^3$

Curved surface area of sphere $= 4\pi r^2$

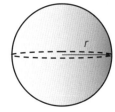

Rate of flow

Example

Water flows through a hosepipe at v centimetres per second.

The cross-sectional area of the hosepipe is A cm². What is the rate of flow?

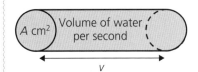

Rate of flow = volume of water per second

In one second water flows v cm along pipe.

So volume of water per second $= v \times A$ cm³

Rate of flow $= Av$ cm³ s⁻¹

Example

The cross-section of a water pipe is a circle of radius 10 cm.

Water flows along the pipe at a depth of 4 cm as shown in the diagram.

(a) Find the cross-sectional area of the water.

(b) If the water is moving at 1.2 m min⁻¹ calculate the volume of water
(in cm³) which flows along the pipe in one hour.

(a) $\cos\theta = \dfrac{6}{10}$ and so $\theta = 53.130\ldots$

So $\angle AOB = 2 \times 53.130\ldots = 106.260\ldots$

Area of sector $OAB = \dfrac{106.3}{360} \times \pi \times 10^2$

$\qquad = 92.729\ldots$ cm² (3 sf)

Area of triangle $OAB = \frac{1}{2} \times 10 \times 10 \times \sin(\angle AOB)$

$\qquad = \frac{1}{2} \times 10 \times 10 \times \sin(106.260°)$

$\qquad = 48$ cm² (3 sf)

Cross-sectional area of water $= 92.729\ldots - 48 = 44.729\ldots$

$\qquad = 44.7$ cm² (3 sf)

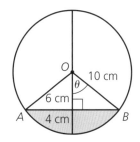

(b) Water travels 1.2 m every minute. This is 120 cm
per minute or 7200 cm per hour.

Volume of water per hour $= Av = 44.729\ldots \times 7200$

$\qquad = 322\,052.6\ldots$ cm³

$\qquad = 322\,000$ cm³ (to 3 sf)

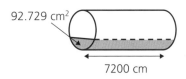

Exam question   CIE 0580 November '06 Paper 4 Q3

Workmen dig a trench in level ground.

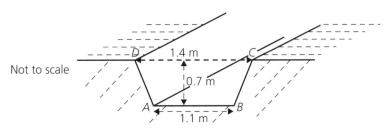

Not to scale

(a) The cross-section of the trench is a trapezium *ABCD* with parallel sides of
length 1.1 m and 1.4 m and a vertical height of 0.7 m.
Calculate the area of the trapezium.

(b) The trench is 500 m long.
Calculate the volume of soil removed.   *(Continued)*

Extended

Exam question (Continued)

(c) One cubic metre of soil has a mass of 4.8 tonnes.
Calculate the mass of soil removed, giving your answer in tonnes and in standard form.

(d) Change your answer to part (c) into grams.

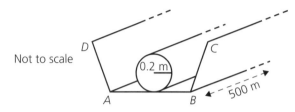

Not to scale

(e) The workmen put a cylindrical pipe, radius 0.2 m and length 500 m, along the bottom of the trench, as shown in the diagram.
Calculate the volume of the cylindrical pipe.

(f) The trench is then refilled with soil.
Calculate the volume of soil put back into the trench as a percentage of the original amount of soil removed.

(a) Area of trapezium $= \frac{1}{2}(a + b)h$

$\qquad = \frac{1}{2}(1.1 + 1.4) \times 0.7$

$\qquad = 0.875 \text{ m}^2$

(b) Volume of trench = cross-sectional area × length

$\qquad = 0.875 \text{ m}^2 \times 500 \text{ m} = 437.5 \text{ m}^3$

(c) Mass of soil $= 437.5 \times 4.8 = 2100 = 2.1 \times 10^3$ tonnes

(d) 1 tonne = 1000 kg

$\qquad = 1000 \times 1000 \text{ g}$

$\qquad = 1\,000\,000 \text{ or } 1 \times 10^6 \text{ g}$

so 2.1×10^3 tonnes

$\qquad = 2.1 \times 10^3 \times 10^6$

$\qquad = 2.1 \times 10^9 \text{ g}$

(e) Volume of pipe $= \pi \times 0.2^2 \times 500$

$\qquad$ is $= 62.8 \text{ m}^3$ (to 3 sf)

Volume of soil put back in is $437.5 - 62.8 = 374.7 \text{ m}^3$

Volume as a percentage of the original amount of soil taken

$= \frac{374.7}{437.5} \times 100 = 85.6\%$ (to 3 sf)

> The trench is in the shape of a prism.

Questions

1. Find the areas of these trapezia by first finding x using Pythagoras' theorem.

(a)

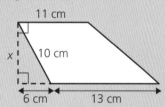

(b)

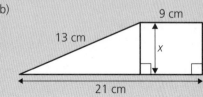

(c)

(d)

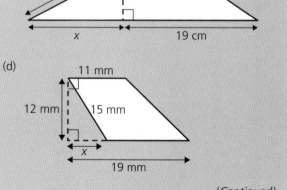

(Continued)

Questions (*Continued*)

2. Find, in terms of π, the area which is enclosed between two circles with the same centre, one with radius 7 cm and the other with radius 5 cm.

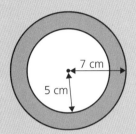

3. Show that the area of a shape consisting of a square of side length 4 cm with a semicircle of radius 2 cm added to one side is $16 + 2\pi$.

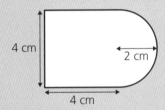

4. Find the radius of the circle which has the same area as the combined area of a circle of radius 12 cm and a circle of radius 5 cm.

5. A running track is 60 m wide. The inside of the inner lane consists of two straight sections of 80 m and two semicircles of radius 24 m.
   (a) Find, in terms of π, the perimeter of the inside of the inner lane.
   (b) Find, in terms of π, the perimeter of the outside of the outer lane.
   (c) Find, in terms of π, the area of the track.

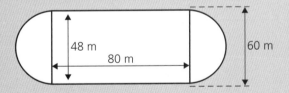

6. A cylindrical glass of radius 4 cm and height 9 cm is filled with water. The water is then poured into a upturned cone of base radius 5 cm and height 15 cm until the cone is full. How much water (to 2 sf) will be left in the glass?

7. A company makes spherical and cubical ice holders. What is the radius (to 3 sf) of the spherical container if it has the same volume as the cubical container with a side length 13 mm?

8. An ice cream scoop is designed to make spheres. Ice cream is taken from a container measuring 20 cm by 15 cm by 13 cm. If the scoop always picks up perfect spheres of radius 2.4 cm how many scoops (to the nearest whole number) can be filled from the container (assuming no waste).

9. A 3-litre pot of paint is used to cover the surface of a large sphere. The instructions say that one litre of paint will cover 5 m². What is the maximum radius of the sphere if it is to be completely covered?

10. A cone of height 45 cm has to hold at least 3 litres of water. What is the least possible value (to 3 sf) of the base radius?

11. A railway tunnel is constructed in the shape of a hollow cylinder. It is 1 km long and has a radius of 3 m. A gravel bed is laid in order to support the track. A cross-section of the tunnel is shown in the diagram, with the shaded area representing the gravel. *AB* represents the horizontal surface of the gravel. *X* is the midpoint of *AB* and $\angle OAB = 60°$.

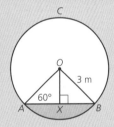

   (a) Show that $OX = 2.60$ m (to 3 sf).
   (b) Find the area (to 3 sf) of the triangle *OAB*.
   (c) By considering the area of the sector *OAB* and your answer to part (b), find (to 3 sf) the shaded area.
   (d) Hence find (to 3 sf) the volume of gravel required for the tunnel.
   (e) Find (to 3 sf) the length of the major arc *ACB*.
   (f) The wall of the tunnel above the gravel level is to be painted. Find (to 3 sf) the surface area to be painted.

12. A ditch is cut in the ground in such a way that its cross-section is a trapezium as shown in the diagram.

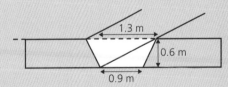

The ditch is 400 m long and it is filled with water.
   (a) What is the area of the cross-section of the ditch?
   (b) What is the volume of water which the ditch contains?
   (c) The water flows at a rate of 1.2 m s⁻¹. How much water passes one point in a minute?
A pipe with a square cross-section in then placed in the ditch and the rest of the ditch is filled in with soil.
   (d) If the pipe has the largest possible cross-section how much soil is put back into the ditch?

31 Trigonometry

Trigonometry is used to find an unknown length or angle in a right-angled triangle.

Pythagoras' theorem

The longest side in a right-angled triangle is called the **hypotenuse**.

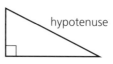

Pythagoras' theorem states that:
"In a right-angled triangle the square on the hypotenuse is equal to the sum of the squares on the other two sides."

$$a^2 + b^2 = c^2$$

Example

Find x and y in these triangles.

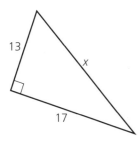

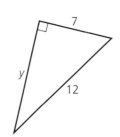

$$13^2 + 17^2 = x^2$$
$$x^2 = 169 + 289 = 458$$
Hence $x = \sqrt{458} = 21.4$ (to 3 sf)

$$y^2 + 7^2 = 12^2$$
So $y^2 = 12^2 - 7^2 = 95$
Hence $y = 9.75$ (to 3 sf)

Example

Find x and y in these triangles.

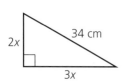

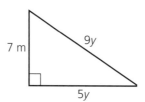

$$(2x)^2 + (3x)^2 = 34^2$$
$$4x^2 + 9x^2 = 1156$$
$$13x^2 = 1156$$
$$x^2 = 88.9$$
$$x = 9.43 \text{ cm (to 3 sf)}$$

$$(9y)^2 - (5y)^2 = 7^2$$
$$81y^2 - 25y^2 = 49$$
$$56y^2 = 49$$
$$y^2 = 0.875$$
$$y = 0.935 \text{ m (to 3 sf)}$$

> Remember $(3x)^2 = 9x^2$ not $3x^2$

Trigonometric ratios

In a right-angled triangle the longest side is the hypotenuse. The other two sides are **opposite** and **adjacent** (next to) the angle θ you are interested in – either because you know its size or because you want to find it.

Remember SOH CAH TOA for right-angled triangles:

$$\mathbf{s}\text{in } \theta = \frac{\mathbf{o}\text{pposite}}{\mathbf{h}\text{ypotenuse}}$$

$$\mathbf{c}\text{os } \theta = \frac{\mathbf{a}\text{djacent}}{\mathbf{h}\text{ypotenuse}}$$

$$\mathbf{t}\text{an } \theta = \frac{\mathbf{o}\text{pposite}}{\mathbf{a}\text{djacent}}$$

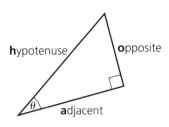

Example
Find x and y in these triangles.

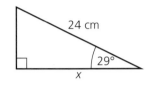

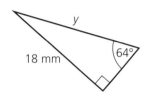

Make sure your calculator is in degrees (**not** radians).

$$\cos 29° = \frac{\text{adjacent}}{\text{hypotenuse}} = \frac{x}{24}$$
$$x = 24 \cos 29°$$
$$= 21.0 \text{ cm (to 3 sf)}$$

$$\sin 64° = \frac{\text{opposite}}{\text{hypotenuse}} = \frac{18}{y}$$
$$y \sin 64° = 18$$
$$y = \frac{18}{\sin 64°}$$
$$= 20.0 \text{ mm (to 3 sf)}$$

```
                    M   Math ▲
24cos(29)

        20.99087297
```

```
                    M   Math ▲
    18
 ‾‾‾‾‾‾
 sin(64)
        20.02683493
```

Example
Find α in this triangle.

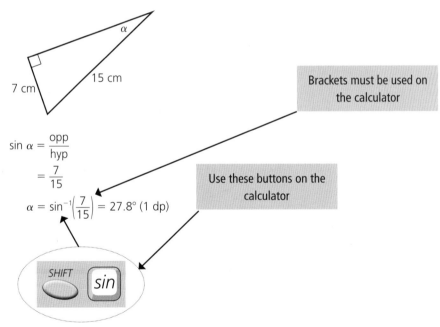

Brackets must be used on the calculator

$$\sin \alpha = \frac{\text{opp}}{\text{hyp}}$$
$$= \frac{7}{15}$$
$$\alpha = \sin^{-1}\left(\frac{7}{15}\right) = 27.8° \text{ (1 dp)}$$

Use these buttons on the calculator

```
                    M   Math ▲
sin⁻¹(7÷15)
        27.81813928
```

Angles of elevation and depression

The angle of **elevation** is the angle you lift your head through to look at something above.

The angle of **depression** is the angle you lower your gaze through to look at something below.

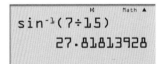

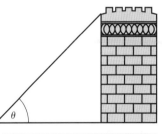

Notice Both angles are measured from the horizontal.

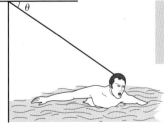

Extended

Example

A surveyor standing on the top of a building 30 m tall sees two points C and D due north of him. The angles of depression of C and D are 35° and 20°. Find the distance CD.

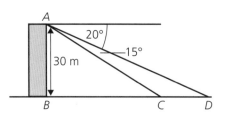
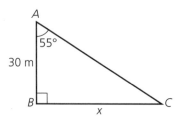

$$\tan 55° = \frac{\text{opp}}{\text{adj}} = \frac{x}{30} \quad \text{so } x = 30 \tan 55° = 42.8 \text{ m (to 3 sf)}$$

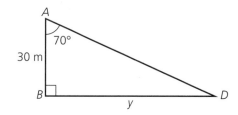

$$\tan 70° = \frac{y}{30} \quad \text{so } y = 30 \tan 70° = 82.4 \text{ m}$$
$$CD = y - x = 82.4 - 42.8 = 39.6 \text{ m (to 3 sf)}$$

Trigonometry in non-right angled triangles

You can also use trigonometry in triangles without a right angle.
Label the sides *a*, *b* and *c*.

Notice that angle *A* is opposite side *a*,
angle *B* is opposite side *b*.
and angle *C* is opposite side *c*.

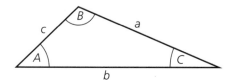

The sine rule

The sine rule states that
$$\frac{a}{\sin A} = \frac{b}{\sin B} = \frac{c}{\sin C}$$

When finding an angle rewrite the rule as
$$\frac{\sin A}{a} = \frac{\sin B}{b} = \frac{\sin C}{c}$$

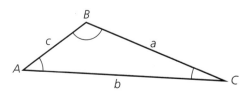

Use the sine rule if you know one side and its opposite angle and one other measurement.

Example

Find *x* and *θ* in these triangles.

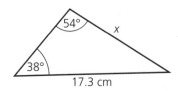
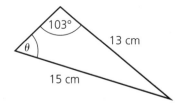

$$\frac{x}{\sin 38°} = \frac{17.3}{\sin 54°}$$

$$x = \frac{17.3 \sin 38°}{\sin 54°}$$

$$= 13.2 \text{ cm (to 3 sf)}$$

$$\frac{\sin \theta}{13} = \frac{\sin 103°}{15}$$

$$\sin \theta = \frac{13 \sin 103°}{15}$$

$$\theta = \sin^{-1}\left(\frac{13 \sin 103°}{15}\right) = 57.6° \text{ (to 1 dp)}$$

Use brackets on the calculator

Cosine rule

The cosine rule states that

$$a^2 = b^2 + c^2 - 2bc \cos A$$

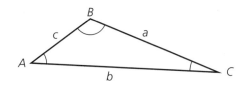

Use the cosine rule if you know
(a) two sides and the enclosed angle (the angle between the two sides)
or
(b) all three sides.

Notice that this is Pythagoras' theorem with a little bit subtracted (or added if $A >$ 90°) to compensate for angle A being less than or greater than 90°.

Example

Find x and θ in these triangles.

$$x^2 = 142^2 + 154^2 - 2 \times 142 \times 154 \cos 32°$$
$$= 6789$$
$$x = 82.4 \text{ cm (to 3 sf)}$$

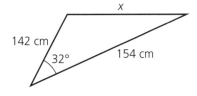

$$24^2 = 32^2 + 19^2 - 2 \times 32 \times 19 \times \cos \theta$$
$$576 = 1385 - 1216 \cos \theta$$
$$\cos \theta = \frac{1385 - 576}{1216}$$
$$\cos \theta = \frac{809}{1216}$$
$$\theta = \cos^{-1}\left(\frac{809}{1216}\right) = 48.3° \text{ (to 1 dp)}$$

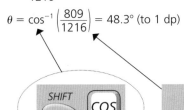

SHIFT   COS

Use brackets on the calculator

Area of triangle

Suppose you know the lengths of a, b and the angle C.

Area $= \frac{1}{2} ab \sin C$

You can use this formula when you know the lengths of two sides in a triangle and the angle between them.

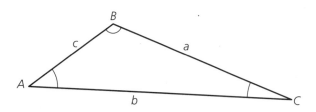

Example

Find the area of this triangle.

Area $= \frac{1}{2} ab \sin C$

$$= \frac{1}{2} \times 154 \times 142 \times \sin 32°$$
$$= 5790 \text{ cm}^2 \text{ (to 3 sf)}$$

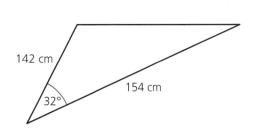

Bearings
Bearings tell you a direction as an angle measured clockwise from the North line.

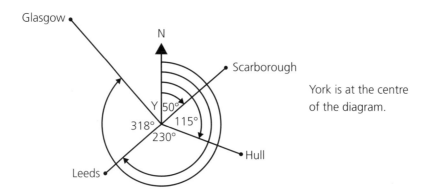

York is at the centre of the diagram.

Scarborough is on a bearing of 050° from York.
Hull is on a bearing of 115° from York.
Leeds is on a bearing of 230° from York. (180° + 50°)
Glasgow is on a bearing of 318° from York.

Example
The bearing of a ship from a lighthouse is 100°.
Find the bearing of the lighthouse from the ship.

Draw a diagram showing the positions of the ship and the lighthouse. Draw the North lines.

The bearing of the lighthouse from the ship is
180° + 100° = 280°

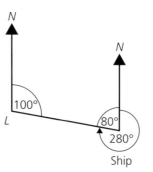

> If you know the bearing of A from B you can work out the bearing of B from A by adding or subtracting 180°.

Example
Clinton walks towards Abi's house on a bearing of 240°.
If Abi sets out to meet Clinton what bearing should she take?

Draw a diagram and put in the North lines.
Abi's bearing is 240° − 180° = 060°

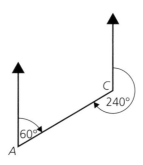

Exam question   CIE 0580 November '06 Paper 4 Q2 a – d

The diagram shows the positions of four cities in Africa, Windhoek (**W**), Johannesburg (**J**), Harari (**H**) and Lusaka (**L**).
WL = 1400 km and **WH** = 1600 km.
Angle LWH = 13°, angle HWJ = 36° and
angle WJH = 95°.

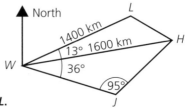

   (a) Calculate the distance **LH**.
   (b) Calculate the distance **WJ**.
   (c) Calculate the area of quadrilateral **WJHL**.
   (d) The bearing of Lusaka from Windhoek is 060°.
       Calculate the bearing of
        (i) Harari from Windhoek.
       (ii) Windhoek from Johannesburg.

(Continued)

Extended

Exam question (Continued)

(a) Use the cosine rule to give

$(LH)^2 = 1400^2 + 1600^2 - 2 \times 1400 \times 1600 \times \cos 13° = 154\,822$

$LH = 393$ km (to 3 sf)

(b) $\angle WHJ = 180° - 36° - 95° = 49°$

Use the sine rule to give

$\dfrac{WJ}{\sin 49°} = \dfrac{1600}{\sin 95°}$ and so $WJ = \dfrac{1600 \sin 49°}{\sin 95°} = 1210$ km (to 3 sf)

(c) Area of $WJHL$ = Area of triangle WLH + area of triangle WJH

Area of $WJHL = \dfrac{1}{2} \times 1400 \times 1600 \times \sin 13° + \dfrac{1}{2} \times 1600 \times 1210 \times \sin 36°$

$= 821\,000$ km^2 (to 3 sf)

(d) (i)

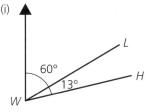

$60° + 13° = 73°$

Bearing of Harari from Windhoek is 073°.

(ii) Bearing of Johannesburg from Windhoek is $60° + 13° + 36° = 109°$

so bearing of Windhoek from Johannesburg is $180° + 109° = 289°$

Trigonometry in three dimensions

The angle between a line and a plane.

The line PQ meets a plane at Q.

The perpendicular line from P meets the plane at R.

The angle θ between the line PQ and the plane is the angle PQR.

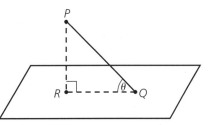

Exam question
CIE 0580 June '06 Paper 4 Q6

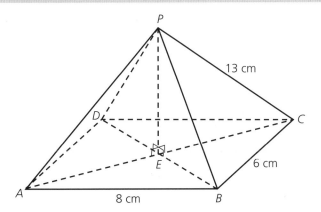

The diagram shows a pyramid on a horizontal rectangular base *ABCD*.

The diagonals of *ABCD* meet at *E*.

***P* is vertically above *E*.**

***AB* = 8 cm, *BC* = 6 cm and *PC* = 13 cm.**

    (a) Calculate *PE*, the height of the pyramid.

    (b) Calculate the volume of the pyramid.

        [The volume of a pyramid is given by $\dfrac{1}{3} \times$ area of base $\times$ height.]

    (c) Calculate angle *PCA*.

(Continued)

Exam question (Continued)

(d) *M* is the midpoint of *AD* and *N* is the midpoint of *BC*.
Calculate angle *MPN*.

(e) (i) Calculate angle *PBC*.

(ii) *K* lies on *PB* so that *BK* = 4 cm.
Calculate the length of *KC*.

(a) Pythagoras' theorem for triangle *ABC* gives

$x^2 = 8^2 + 6^2 = 100$

$x = 10$ cm

So *AE* is $\frac{10}{2} = 5$ cm

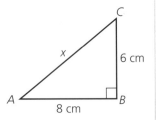

Draw a diagram of the part of the figure you are working on.

Pythagoras' theorem for triangle *AEP* gives

$13^2 = 5^2 + h^2$

$169 = 25 + h^2$

$h^2 = 144$

$h = 12$ cm

$PE = 12$ cm

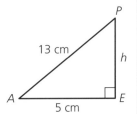

$PA = PC = 13$ cm

(b) Volume of pyramid = $\frac{1}{3} \times$ (base area) $\times$ height

Volume of pyramid = $\frac{1}{3} \times 48 \times 12 = 192$ cm³

Base area = 8 × 6 = 48 cm²
Height = 12 cm

(c) The angle $\angle PCE = \angle PCA$
Using SOHCAHTOA gives

$\cos \theta = \frac{5}{13}$ and so $\theta = \cos^{-1}\left(\frac{5}{13}\right) = 67.4°$ (to 1 dp)

$\angle PCA = 67.4°$

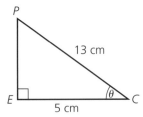

(d) Using SOHCAHTOA gives

$\tan \alpha = \frac{4}{12}$ and so $\alpha = \tan^{-1}\left(\frac{4}{12}\right) = 18.43...°$

$\angle MPN = 2 \times \angle NPE$

$= 2 \times 18.43...°$

$= 36.9°$ (to 1 dp)

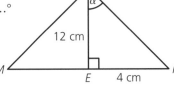

(e) (i) $\angle PBC = \angle PBN = \beta$

Using SOHCAHTOA gives

$\cos \beta = \frac{3}{13}$ and so $\beta = \cos^{-1}\left(\frac{3}{13}\right) = 76.7°$ (to 1 dp)

$\angle PBC = 76.7°$ (to 1 dp)

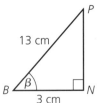

(ii) Cosine rule gives

$z^2 = 4^2 + 6^2 - 2 \times 4 \times 6 \times \cos 76.7°$

$= 40.95...$

$KC = 6.40$ cm (to 3 sf)

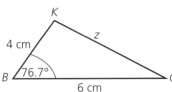

Questions

1. A piece of A4 paper measures 298 mm by 210 mm. Find the length of the longest straight line which can be drawn on it.

2. A square field has side length 45 m. Find the length of the diagonal (to 3 sf).

3. A man walks 1.5 km north and then 1 km east. How far is he from his starting point (to the nearest m)?

4. An equilateral triangle has side length 8 cm. Find the height of the triangle (to 3 sf).

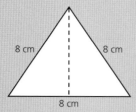

5. In the trapezium AD = 32 cm, FE = 20 cm, FB = 12 cm and angle FAB = 60°.

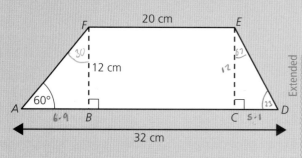

(a) Show that AB = 6.9 cm (to 1 dp).
(b) By first finding CD, calculate the angle EDC, giving your answer to the nearest degree.
(c) Find the area of the trapezium.

6. In the diagram:

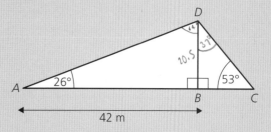

(a) show that the length BD is 20.5 m (to 2 sf).
(b) use this to calculate the length DC (to 2 sf).
(c) calculate the angle ADC.

7. In the diagram D is the midpoint of AB.

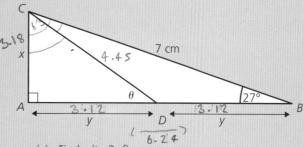

(a) Find x (to 3 sf).
(b) Find y (to 3 sf).
(c) Hence show that $\theta = 45.5°$ (to 1 dp).

8. A car travels 15 km from A on a bearing of 100° to a point B. It then travels 12 km from B on a bearing of 175° to a point C. The car then returns to A.
(a) Calculate the area enclosed by this journey (to 3 sf).
(b) Calculate the time (to the nearest minute) it takes to travel from C to A if the car maintains a steady speed of 80 km h⁻¹.

(*Continued*)

Questions (*Continued*)

9.

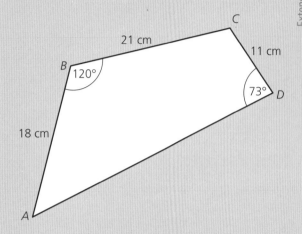

(a) Find the length of *AC* (to 3 sf) in the quadrilateral.
(b) Find the area (to 3 sf) of the triangle *ABC*.
(c) Find the angle *CAD* (to 1 dp) and so find the angle *ACD* (to 1 dp).
(d) Hence find the area of the quadrilateral *ABCD* (to 2 sf).

10. In the pyramid *ABCDE*, the square base *ABCD* is horizontal and *EM* is vertical. *M* is the midpoint of *AC*. *AB* = 15 cm and *EM* = 11 cm.

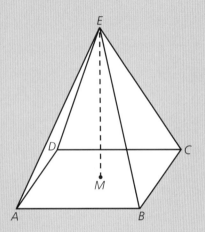

(a) Find *AM* (to 3 sf).
(b) Show that *AE* = 15.3 cm (to 3 sf).
(c) Calculate the angle (to 1 dp) between the line *AE* and the plane *ABCD*.

32 Statistics

Pie charts

In a pie chart you use sectors to represent the data.

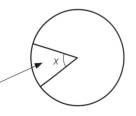

An angle of x in the pie represents $\frac{x}{360}$ of the total.

Example

The pie chart shows the answers 120 students gave to a question on a multiple choice paper. How many students put A as the answer?

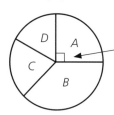

The right angle in the sector representing A shows that $\frac{90}{360}$ or one-quarter of the candidates chose A as their answer.

$\frac{1}{4}$ of $120 = \frac{1}{4} \times 120 = 30$

30 students gave the answer A.

Example

James asked 36 pupils in his class where they had been on holiday. He recorded the results in this table:

Country	UK	France	Spain	Other
Number of pupils	9	6	11	10

Represent this information on a pie chart.

At the centre of the pie there is an angle of 360°. There are 36 pupils so 10° represents one pupil.

Country	UK	France	Spain	Other
Number of pupils	9	6	11	10
Angle of sector	90°	60°	110°	100°

Example

The pie chart shows the nationalities of a group of 150 delegates at a conference. Given that 30 delegates came from Ethiopia, find:
(a) the values of p and q
(b) how many delegates came from the other countries.

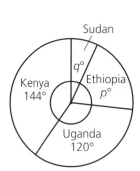

(a) 30 out of 150 are from Ethiopia. So one-fifth of the delegates are from Ethiopia.

Hence $p = \frac{1}{5} \times 360° = 72°$

It follows that $q = 360° - 72° - 144° - 120° = 24°$

(b) Number from Kenya is $\frac{144}{360} \times 150 = 60$

Number from Uganda is $\frac{120}{360} \times 150 = 50$

Number from Sudan is $\frac{24}{360} \times 150 = 10$

Pictograms

In a pictogram you use symbols or pictures to represent data. For example, you could use
to represent ten pupils in a school.

If the numbers in a school are:

Year	Frequency
7	80
8	75
9	70
10	70
11	100

You could represent the data like this:

Year	Frequency
7	👤👤👤👤👤👤👤👤
8	👤👤👤👤👤👤👤🯲
9	👤👤👤👤👤👤👤
10	👤👤👤👤👤👤👤
11	👤👤👤👤👤👤👤👤👤👤

Note that half a person represents 5 pupils.

Bar charts

The homework scores of 20 pupils were as follows:

20	20	15	20	17
16	18	18	20	15
20	18	19	17	18
20	19	18	20	18

Putting the scores in a table gives:

Score	Frequency
15	2
16	1
17	2
18	6
19	2
20	7

From the table you can draw a bar chart. The heights of the bars represent the frequencies.

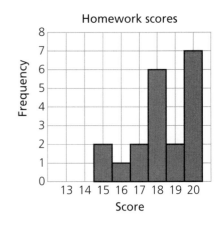

Homework scores

Scatter diagrams

You can use a scatter diagram to find out if there is any correlation (connection) between two sets of variables, such as shoe size and height or sales of gloves and the temperature.

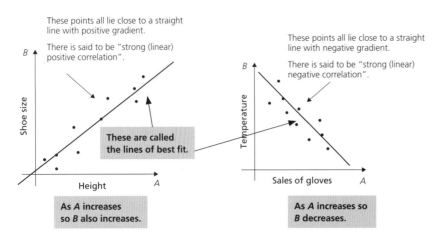

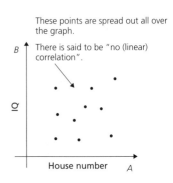

Mean, median, mode and range

The **mean** is $\dfrac{\text{sum of all the values}}{\text{number of values}}$, which can be written as $\bar{x} = \dfrac{\Sigma x}{n}$

The **median** is the "middle" value when the data have been written in ascending or descending order. If there are n values then the median is the $\dfrac{n+1}{2}$th value.

When n is odd…
      For example with 3 values, the median is the $\dfrac{3+1}{2}$ = second value.

When n is even…
      For example with 4 values, the median is the $\dfrac{4+1}{2}$ = 2.5th value, that is halfway between the second and third values.

The **mode** is the value which appears most frequently.

The **range** is the difference between the largest and smallest values.

Example
Find the mean, median, mode and range of 14, 16, 10, 15, 13, 13, 19, 15, 13, 12, 14.

(a)   Mean $= \dfrac{14 + 16 + 10 + 15 + 13 + 13 + 19 + 15 + 13 + 12 + 14}{11} = \dfrac{154}{11} = 14$

(b)   First write the data in ascending order…
                    10, 12, 13, 13, 13, (14,) 14, 15, 15, 16, 19

       Median = 14

(c)   Mode = 13

(d)   Range = 19 − 10 = 9

> **There are 11 values and so the median is the $\dfrac{11+1}{2}$ = sixth value**

Discrete and continuous data

Data that can take only certain values is called **discrete**. So, for example, shoe size is discrete since it can take only certain values.

Data you obtain by measuring can take any value in a given range and is called **continuous**. So, foot length, for example, is continuous.

Grouped data (discrete)
Discrete data are sometimes given in a long list but more often they are given in a table, grouped into different categories.

Example
The scores of a class in a test are given in the table.

Score (x)	11	12	13	14	15	16
Frequency (f)	2	5	7	6	3	1

Find the mean and the mode.

Mean score $= \dfrac{\text{sum of all the values}}{\text{number of values}}$

$$= \dfrac{\overbrace{11 + 11}^{11 \times 2} + \overbrace{12 + 12 + 12 + 12 + 12}^{12 \times 5} + 13 + \ldots + 15 + 15 + 15 + 16}{2 + 5 + 7 + 6 + 3 + 1}$$

You could write this as $\dfrac{11 \times 2 + 12 \times 5 + 13 \times 7 + 14 \times 6 + 15 \times 3 + 16 \times 1}{2 + 5 + 7 + 6 + 3 + 1} = \dfrac{318}{24} = 13.25$

The mode is the score with the highest frequency, that is 13.

Extended

Grouped data (continuous)

Continuous data can take any value in a given range and is usually grouped in classes.

Example

The table shows the masses, in grams, of 100 apples. Find the mean mass of the apples.

Mass, x (g)	120–	130–	140–	150–	160–	170–180
Frequency	25	19	23	16	12	5

The mass of each individual apple is not known. The masses will be spread out over the range for each class, but it is reasonable to suppose that the mean weight of the apples in each class will be at the midpoint of that class. Adjusting the table gives:

Mass, x (g)	125	135	145	155	165	175
Frequency	25	19	23	16	12	5

Mean mass of all the apples = $\bar{x}$

$$\bar{x} = \frac{125 \times 25 + 135 \times 19 + 145 \times 23 + 155 \times 16 + 165 \times 12 + 175 \times 5}{25 + 19 + 23 + 16 + 12 + 5} = \frac{14\,360}{100}$$

$$= 143.6\,\text{g (to 1 dp)}$$

> $\bar{x}$ (x bar) is used to denote the mean.

NB This is only an estimate of the mean as the actual mass of each apple is not known.

> Remember to include the units.

Since the actual mass of each individual apple in the example above is not known, the mode cannot be stated. The "**modal group**" can be found, that is the group with the highest frequency. In this example it is "120–".

The median is the $\frac{100}{2} = $ 50th value after sorting the masses into order.

> **When the total frequency n is large the median can be calculated using the $\frac{n}{2}$ value and not the $\left(\frac{n+1}{2}\right)$ value**

The lightest 25 apples were in the "120-" category and the next 19 lightest apples were in the "130-" category. The 50th apple must be in the "140-" category and to find out just where the median lies within this category you use a cumulative frequency diagram.

Cumulative frequency diagram

Mass, x (g)	120–	130–	140–	150–	160–	170–180
Frequency	25	19	23	16	12	5

From the table you can see that no apple had a mass below 120 g, that 25 apples had a mass below 130 g, that 25 + 19 = 44 apples were under 140 g etc.

25, 44, 67 etc. are called the cumulative frequencies. You can show the cumulative frequencies in the frequency table.

Mass x(g)	Frequency	Cumulative frequency	
$120 \leqslant x < 130$	25	25	
$130 \leqslant x < 140$	19	44	25 + 19
$140 \leqslant x < 150$	23	67	44 + 23
$150 \leqslant x < 160$	16	83	
$160 \leqslant x < 170$	12	95	
$170 \leqslant x < 180$	5	100	

A cumulative frequency curve is a curve which displays this information with the cumulative frequency on the *y*-axis and the *upper boundaries* of class intervals on the *x*-axis. Each cumulative frequency is plotted at the upper end of its class interval.

The cumulative frequency curve *must always start* on the *x*-axis. In this example since no apples had a mass below 120 g it will start at 120 on the *x*-axis.

Example
Plot a cumulative frequency for the data shown in the table above.

Plot the points (120, 0), (130, 25) etc.

The median can be read off the cumulative frequency curve as shown below

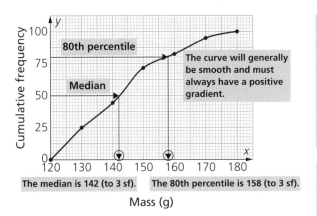

The median is 142 (to 3 sf).   The 80th percentile is 158 (to 3 sf).

Mass (g)

Median
To read off the median:
- Calculate half the total frequency on the *y*-axis (i.e. 50 in this example)
- Draw a horizontal line to the graph at this value
- Read down to the *x*-axis.

Percentiles
The 80th percentile is the value below which 80% of the values lie.

Quartiles
The lower quartile (the 25th percentile) and the upper quartile (the 75th percentile) can be read off the cumulative frequency diagram in the same way.

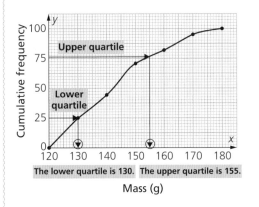

The lower quartile is 130. The upper quartile is 155.

Mass (g)

Quartiles
To read off the quartiles:
- Calculate one-quarter and three-quarters of the total frequency on the *y*-axis (i.e. 25 and 75 in this example).
- Draw horizontal lines to the graph at these values.
- Read down to the *x*-axis.

Interquartile range = upper quartile − lower quartile
= 155 − 130 = 25

Exam question   CIE 0580 November '05 Paper 4 Q9

The heights (*h* cm) of 270 students in a school are measured and the results are shown in the table.

h	Frequency
$120 < h \leq 130$	15
$130 < h \leq 140$	24
$140 < h \leq 150$	36
$150 < h \leq 160$	45
$160 < h \leq 170$	50
$170 < h \leq 180$	43
$180 < h \leq 190$	37
$190 < h \leq 200$	20

(Continued)

Extended

Exam question (Continued)

(a) Write down the modal group.

(b) (i) Calculate an estimate of the mean height.

    (ii) Explain why the answer to part (b)(i) is an estimate.

(c) The following table shows the cumulative frequencies for the heights of the students.

h	Cumulative frequency
$h \leqslant 120$	0
$h \leqslant 130$	p
$h \leqslant 140$	q
$h \leqslant 150$	r
$h \leqslant 160$	120
$h \leqslant 170$	170
$h \leqslant 180$	213
$h \leqslant 190$	250
$h \leqslant 200$	270

Write down the values of p, q and r.

(d) Using a scale of 1 cm to 5 units, draw a horizontal h-axis, starting at $h = 120$.

    Using a scale of 1 cm to 20 units on the vertical axis, draw a cumulative frequency diagram.

(e) Use your diagram to find

    (i) the median height

    (ii) the upper quartile

    (iii) the interquartile range

    (iv) the 60th percentile.

(f) All the players in the school's basketball team are chosen from the 30 tallest students. Use your diagram to find the least possible height of any player in the basketball team.

(a) The modal group is the group with the highest frequency, that is $160 < h \leqslant 170$ cm

(b) (i) Use midpoints for each group as follows

Height, h (cm)	125	135	145	155	165	175	185	195
Frequency	15	24	36	45	50	43	37	20

So the mean is

$$\bar{x} = \frac{125 \times 15 + 135 \times 24 + 145 \times 36 + 155 \times 45 + 165 \times 50 + 175 \times 43 + 185 \times 37 + 195 \times 20}{15 + 24 + 36 + 45 + 50 + 43 + 37 + 20}$$

$$= \frac{43\,830}{270} = 162.3 \text{ cm (to 1 dp)}$$

(ii) This is an estimate because midpoints have been used. The actual heights of the students are not known.

(c) Use the table on page 129 to find the cumulative frequencies.

h	Cumulative frequency
$h \leqslant 120$	0
$h \leqslant 130$	$p = 15$
$h \leqslant 140$	$q = 15 + 24 = 39$
$h \leqslant 150$	$r = 39 + 36 = 75$
$h \leqslant 160$	120
$h \leqslant 170$	170
$h \leqslant 180$	213
$h \leqslant 190$	250
$h \leqslant 200$	270

So $p = 15$, $q = 39$ and $r = 75$.

(Continued)

Extended

Exam question (Continued)

(d)

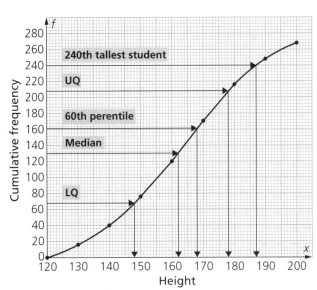

(e) Total number of students is 270.

(i) Median is height of the $\frac{270}{2}$ = 135th student. This is 162 cm.

(ii) Upper quartile is height of the $\frac{270}{4}$ x 3 = 202.5th student. This is 178 cm.

(iii) Lower quartile is height of the $\frac{270}{4}$ = 67.5th student. This is 148 cm.

Interquartile range is 178 − 148 = 30 cm

(iv) 60th percentile is height of the $\frac{270}{100} \times 60$ = 162nd student. This is 168 cm.

(f) The shortest person in the team is the 240th tallest student in the school. Reading off the graph this is 187 cm.

Histograms

Histograms with equal class intervals are in the Core part of the syllabus and those with unequal class intervals are in the Extended part of the syllabus.

Suppose the data in this table are represented in a bar chart.

Length (h)	Frequency
650-	3
670-	7
680-	20
690-	16
700-750	4

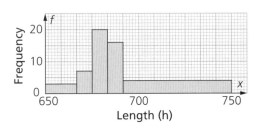

The bar chart is misleading as the bar for the 4 people in the class "700–750" has the same area as the bar for the 20 people in the "680–" class.

This is always a problem unless the bar chart is for data in which all the class widths are equal.

To overcome this problem you use a graph in which the **area** of each block represents the **frequency**. The name for this type of graph is a **histogram** and it is used when the class widths are different.

In a histogram the **area of each block is proportional to the frequency**.

The area of the block (width × height) = the frequency,

so height $= \dfrac{\text{frequency}}{\text{width}}$

The height of the bar is called the **frequency density** since it shows how densely populated each class width is.

So frequency density $= \dfrac{\text{frequency}}{\text{class width}}$ where the "class width" is the width of the interval (i.e. it runs from the lower boundary to the upper boundary)
Frequency density = Frequency divided by class width

Be careful with class width.

Length (h)	Frequency
650-	3
670-	7

Weight (w)	Frequency
15-19	2
20-25	10

Class width of "650–" is 20 since it means $650 \leqslant h < 670$.

Class width of "15–19" is 5 since it means $14.5 \leqslant w < 19.5$.

Exam question
CIE 0580 June '06 Paper 4 Q9

(a) The numbers 0, 1, 1, 1, 2, k, m, 6, 9, 9 are in order ($k \neq m$).
   Their median is 2.5 and their mean is 3.6.
   (i) Write down the mode.
   (ii) Find the value of k.
   (iii) Find the value of m.
   (iv) Maria chooses a number at random from the list.
      The probability of choosing this number is $\frac{1}{5}$. Which number does she choose?
(b) 100 students are given a question to answer.
   The time taken (t seconds) by each student is recorded and the results are shown in the table.

t	$0 < t \leqslant 20$	$20 < t \leqslant 30$	$30 < t \leqslant 35$	$35 < t \leqslant 40$	$40 < t \leqslant 50$	$50 < t \leqslant 60$	$60 < t \leqslant 80$
Frequency	10	10	15	28	22	7	8

   (i) Calculate an estimate of the mean time taken.
   (ii) Two students are picked at random.
      What is the probability that they both took more than 50 seconds?
      Give your answer as a fraction in its lowest terms.

   Answer part (c) on a sheet of graph paper.
(c) The data in part (b) is regrouped to give the following table.

t	$0 < t \leqslant 30$	$30 < t \leqslant 60$	$60 < t \leqslant 80$
Frequency	p	q	8

   (i) Write down the values of p and q.
   (ii) Draw an accurate histogram to show these results.
      Use a scale of 1 cm to represent 5 seconds on the horizontal time axis.
      Use a scale of 1 cm to 0.2 units of frequency density (so that 1 cm² on your histogram represents 1 student).

(a) (i) The mode is the value which appears most frequently, that is 1.
   (ii) There are 10 values and so the median is the $\frac{10 + 1}{2} = 5.5$th. This is the mean of the fifth and sixth values.

(Continued)

Extended

Exam question (Continued)

The fifth value is 2 and the 6th value is k. So the median is $\frac{k + 2}{2}$.

It is given that the median is 2.5 so $\frac{k + 2}{2} = 2.5$

Hence $k + 2 = 5$ and so $k = 3$.

(iii) The mean given as is $\frac{0 + 1 + 1 + 1 + 2 + 3 + m + 6 + 9 + 9}{10}$ and the

mean is given as 3.6, so $\frac{0 + 1 + 1 + 1 + 2 + 3 + m + 6 + 9 + 9}{10} = 3.6$

It follows that $32 + m = 10 \times 3.6$ and so $m = 36 - 32 = 4$

(iv) The probability of Maria choosing her number is $\frac{1}{5}$. This is the same as $\frac{2}{10}$.

There are ten numbers in total so her number must appear twice. It follows that her number must be 9.

(b) (i) Make a table showing the frequencies and the midpoint of each class.

Time	$\frac{0+20}{2}$ 10	$\frac{20+30}{2}$ 25	$\frac{30+35}{2}$ 32.5	$\frac{35+40}{2}$ 37.5	$\frac{40+50}{2}$ 45	$\frac{50+60}{2}$ 55	$\frac{60+80}{2}$ 70
Frequency	10	10	15	28	22	7	8

$$\bar{x} = \frac{10 \times 10 + 25 \times 10 + 32.5 \times 15 + 37.5 \times 28 + 45 \times 22 + 55 \times 7 + 70 \times 8}{10 + 10 + 15 + 28 + 22 + 7 + 8}$$

$$= \frac{3822.5}{100} = 38.225$$

(ii) The 7 students in the $50 < t \leqslant 60$ class and the 8 students in the $60 < t \leqslant 80$ class took more than 50 seconds.

So the probability that the first student chosen takes more than 50 seconds is $\frac{15}{100}$.

There are now 99 students to choose from, of whom 14 took more than 50 seconds. So the probability that the second student chosen takes more than 50 seconds is $\frac{14}{99}$.

Probability that both students take more than 50 seconds is $\frac{15}{100} \times \frac{14}{99} = \frac{210}{9900} = \frac{7}{330}$.

(c) (i) Combining the first two classes in the initial table gives $p = 10 + 10 = 20$

Combining the next four classes in the initial table gives $q = 15 + 28 + 22 + 7 = 72$.

(ii)

Time	$10 < t \leqslant 30$	$30 < t \leqslant 60$	$60 < t \leqslant 80$
Frequency	20	72	8
Frequency density	$\frac{20}{20} = 1$	$\frac{72}{30} = 2.4$	$\frac{8}{20} = 0.4$

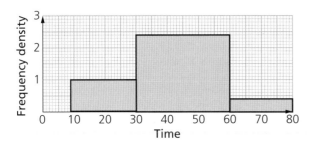

Questions

1. Describe the correlation shown in the scatter diagram.

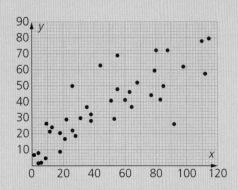

2. Find the mean, median, mode and range of these sets of numbers by first writing the numbers in ascending order.

(a) 3   5   8   1   2   3   13

(b) 13   19   22   25   29   11   20   22
    34   28

(c) 1.03   1.07   1.21   1.05   1.29   0.95

(d) 1   7   3   9   10   13   13

(e) 42   41   45   46   48   51   51   52

(f) 119   113   108   109   112   114   103
    119   120

(g) 89   81   82   85   87   88   90   91
    92   95   88

3. (a) In question 2(c) what would the mean and median be if the largest value, i.e. 1.29 was replaced with 4.29?

(b) What can you say about the effect on the mean and on the median when the largest number in a set of data is replaced with a very large number?

4. A die was rolled many times and its score (*x*) is shown in the table.

x	1	2	3	4	5	6
f	3	8	13	10	6	5

(a) Find the mean of the frequency distribution (to 3 sf).

(b) Find the median of the frequency distribution.

(c) Write down the mode and the range of the frequency distribution.

5. The table shows the masses of 175 children.

Mass, *x* (kg)	40–	45–	50–
Frequency	43	31	39

	55–	60–	65–70
	28	19	15

(a) Find the midpoint of the "40-" class interval.

(b) Draw a table with midpoints against frequency.

(c) Use this table to find an estimate of the mean (to 3 sf).

(d) Find the class interval in which the median lies.

6. The table below shows the time it took for a group of 100 commuters to get to work:

Time taken, *x* (min)	55–59	60–64	65–69
Frequency	21	17	22

	70–74	75–79	80–84
	16	13	11

(a) Copy and complete the following table with midpoints against frequency.

Time taken, *x* (min)		62	
Frequency	21	17	22

		77	
	16	13	11

(b) Use this table to find an estimate of the mean (to 3 sf).

7. The masses (in kg) of 100 animals are recorded in the table.

Mass (kg)	20–	25–	30–	35–
Frequency	8	21	28	19

	40–	45–50
	15	9

Write down the coordinates of the points through which the cumulative frequency curve should pass.

8. The masses of a group of 80 competitors in a sports tournament are recorded in the table.

Mass (kg)	55–	60–	65–	70–
Frequency	5	12	24	23

	75–	80–	85–90
	14	1	1

(a) Without any calculations, state in which class the median must lie.

(b) How many competitors had a mass below 55 kg?

(c) How many competitors had a mass below 85 kg?

(*Continued*)

Questions (*Continued*)

(d) Draw a cumulative frequency graph. Use a scale of 2 cm per 5 units on the horizontal axis and 1 cm per 5 units on the vertical axis. (The horizontal axis should go from 55 kg to 90 kg).

(e) Use the graph to find an estimate for the median.

9. A biologist recorded the lengths of a group of 200 insects and displayed his results in the table.

Length (mm)	10–	11–	12–	13–
Frequency	17	38	53	49

	14–	15–	16–17
	21	12	10

(a) Draw a cumulative frequency graph for these data using a scale of 2 cm per 1 mm on the horizontal axis and 1 cm per 10 units on the vertical axis. (The horizontal axis should go from 10 mm to 17 mm).

(b) Use the graph to find an estimate of the median.

(c) Use the graph to find estimates of the lower and upper quartiles.

10. The table records the time taken for a group of 220 candidates to finish a task.

Time taken (min)	$5 \leqslant t < 10$	$10 \leqslant t < 15$
Number of candidates	32	56

	$15 \leqslant t < 20$	$20 \leqslant t < 25$	$25 \leqslant t < 30$
	61	42	29

(a) Draw a cumulative frequency graph using a scale of 2 cm per 5 units on the horizontal axis and 1 cm per 10 units on the vertical axis. (The horizontal axis should go from 5 min to 30 min).

(b) Use the graph to estimate the median time taken to complete the task.

(c) Estimate how long it took for the first 150 candidates to finish the task.

(d) Estimate how many candidates finished in under 18 minutes.

11. At a girls' school, a random sample of pupils was taken and each pupil recorded her intake of milk (in ml) during a given day.

Some of the results and part of the histogram are shown.

Milk intake (ml)	10–	30–	60–	100–
No. of pupils	4	9	32	
Frequency density				

150–	200–	300–500
25		

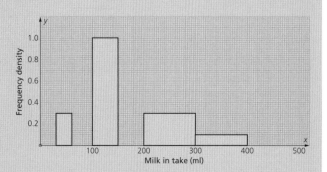

(a) Calculate the frequency density for the "30– " category.

(b) Copy the table, calculating the frequency density in all the cases where the number of students is stated.

(c) Copy and complete the histogram to illustrate these data using 1 cm per 50 ml on the horizontal axis and 1 cm per 0.1 on the vertical axis. Use the table to complete the histogram.

(d) Use the histogram to complete the table.

12. Summarised below are the prices of the goods (to the nearest £) sold by an electrical shop on a certain day.

Price of goods (£)	Frequency	Frequency Density
$20 < x \leqslant 40$	20	1
$40 < x \leqslant 50$	37	
$50 < x \leqslant 60$		6.2
$60 < x \leqslant 70$	51	
$70 < x \leqslant 90$	30	
$90 < x \leqslant 130$		0.2

(*Continued*)

Extended

Questions (*Continued*)

(a) Copy and complete the table.

(b) Draw a histogram to illustrate these data using 1 cm per £10 on the horizontal axis (from 20 to 130) and 2 cm per unit on the vertical axis (from 0 to 7).

13. A boy drew a histogram for the data shown in the table. He added a column for the width of each bar to the table.

Mass (kg)	Frequency	Frequency density (height of bar)	Width of bar
10-	8		
30-	16		
50-	38		
60-	40	8 cm	1 cm
70-	28		
75-	30		
80-	21		
85-	11		
90-120	6		

On the boy's histogram the "60-" bar was 1 cm wide and 8 cm high as shown in the table.

(a) Copy and complete the table.

(b) Hence draw the boy's histogram using the scale that he used.

33 Probability

Probability tells you how likely or unlikely it is that an event will occur.
Examples of probability:

The probability of Tottenham Hotspur winning their next game is 0.75.
The probability of scoring a six when a die is thrown is $\frac{1}{6}$.
The probability of a part made in a factory being faulty is 0.02.

Probabilities can be expressed either as a fraction or a decimal.
All probabilities lie between 0 and 1.

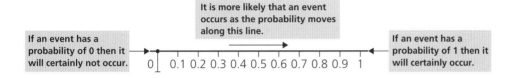

| If an event has a probability of 0 then it will certainly not occur. | It is more likely that an event occurs as the probability moves along this line. | If an event has a probability of 1 then it will certainly occur. |

0 0.1 0.2 0.3 0.4 0.5 0.6 0.7 0.8 0.9 1

P(event not happening) = 1 − P(event happening)

Example

The probability of the traffic lights being red is 0.3.
The probability of them being green is $\frac{1}{2}$.
(a) Is it more likely that the lights are red or green?
(b) Find the probability that the lights are not red.

(a)

0 0.1 0.2 0.3 0.4 0.5 0.6 0.7 0.8 0.9 1

The probability of the traffic lights being red is 0.3. This can be written as P(the traffic lights being red) = 0.3

The probability of the traffic lights being green is $\frac{1}{2}$, or 0.5. P(the traffic lights being green) = 0.5

So it is more likely that the lights are green since 0.5 is greater than 0.3.

(b) P(the traffic lights not being red) = 1 − P(the traffic lights being red)
= 1 − 0.3 = 0.7

Relative frequency
The **relative frequency** of an event happening is defined as

$$\text{relative frequency} = \frac{\text{number of times event happens}}{\text{total number of trials}}$$

Mutually exclusive events
Two events A and B are said to be **mutually exclusive** if they cannot happen at the same time (e.g. scoring a 3 on a die and scoring a 6 on a die are mutually exclusive).

If A and B are mutually exclusive then

Probability of A or B happening = Probability of A happening + Probability of B happening.
P(A or B) = P(A) + P(B)

Example

There are 7 red balls, 2 blue balls and 6 yellow balls in a bag. A ball is chosen out of the bag. What is the probability that the ball is:

(a) blue

(b) red

(c) either red or blue.

(a) 2 out of 15 of the balls are blue so the probability of picking a blue ball is $\frac{2}{15}$.

(b) 7 out of 15 of the balls are red so the probability of picking a red ball is $\frac{7}{15}$.

(c) The events of being red and blue are mutually exclusive so:

Probability of ball being red or blue = Probability of being red + Probability of being blue

$$= \frac{7}{15} + \frac{2}{15}$$
$$= \frac{9}{15}$$
$$= \frac{3}{5}$$

Example

A spinner is equally likely to land on the numbers 1, 2, 3, 4, 5 or 6.

Find the probability that the spinner lands on:

(a) an even number

(b) a number greater than 4

(c) an even number or a number greater than 4

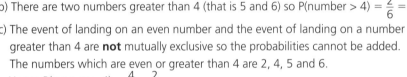

(a) There are three even numbers (that is 2, 4, 6) so P(even number) $= \frac{3}{6} = \frac{1}{2}$

(b) There are two numbers greater than 4 (that is 5 and 6) so P(number > 4) $= \frac{2}{6} = \frac{1}{3}$

(c) The event of landing on an even number and the event of landing on a number greater than 4 are **not** mutually exclusive so the probabilities cannot be added.

The numbers which are even or greater than 4 are 2, 4, 5 and 6.

Hence P(even or > 4) $= \frac{4}{6} = \frac{2}{3}$

Example

The probability of a girl in a school wearing glasses is 0.3 and the probability of a girl having blonde hair is 0.4. Joshua thinks that the probability of a girl wearing glasses or having blonde hair is 0.7. Is he right?

Joshua is not right.

Some girls have blonde hair and wear glasses. In other words, wearing glasses and having blonde hair are not mutually exclusive, so their probabilities cannot be added together.

Combined events

Two events A and B are said to be **independent** if they have no effect on each other (e.g. being late to school in Kenya and raining in Bolivia are independent).

If A and B are **independent** events then

P(A happening and B happening) = P(A happening) × P(B happening).

Example

A coin is tossed and a die is rolled. Find the probability of getting a head on the coin and a five on the die.

Suppose the event A is getting a head on the coin and that the event B is getting a five on the die.

P(A) $= \frac{1}{2}$ and P(B) $= \frac{1}{6}$.

These are independent events so P(A and B) = P(A) × P(B) $= \frac{1}{2} \times \frac{1}{6} = \frac{1}{12}$

Extended

Example

Alexander shoots three arrows at a target. With each arrow, the probability that he hits the target is 0.3. Whether he hits with any given arrow is independent of what happened to the previous arrows.

Find the probability that he hits with the first two arrows but misses with the third.

The probability that he hits the target with his first arrow is 0.3.

The probability that he hits the target with his second arrow is 0.3.

The probability that he misses the target with his third arrow is $1 - 0.3 = 0.7$.

Since the events are assumed to be independent, the probability that he hits with the first and hits with the second and misses with the third is obtained by multiplying the three probabilities.

So P(hits with first two and misses with third) = $0.3 \times 0.3 \times 0.7 = 0.063$

Tree diagrams

Tree diagrams are a clear way of representing the possible outcomes of combined events.

On tree diagrams:

as you move across multiply probabilities

as you move **D**own a**DD** probabilities.

> Questions often involve choosing two or more balls from a bag. In these questions it is important to establish whether or not the first ball has been replaced before the next one has been chosen.
> **Read the question carefully.**

Ball replaced

Example

A bag contains 10 balls, seven of which are red and the rest green. A boy takes out a ball from the bag, notes its colour and *puts it back*. He then repeats this process.

(a) Draw a tree diagram to represent this information.

(b) Find the probability that he chooses two red balls.

(c) Find the probability that he chooses two balls of different colours.

(a)

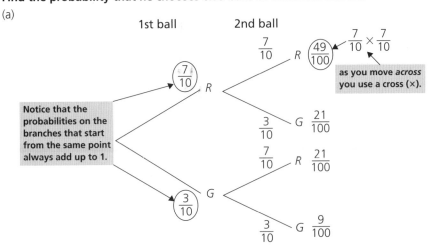

(b) Probability of two reds is $\frac{7}{10} \times \frac{7}{10} = \frac{49}{100}$ (move *across* so use a cross ($\times$))

(c) P(RG) = $\frac{7}{10} \times \frac{3}{10} = \frac{21}{100}$ and P(GR) = $\frac{3}{10} \times \frac{7}{10} = \frac{21}{100}$

As you move **D**own a**DD** so probability is $\frac{21}{100} + \frac{21}{100} = \frac{42}{100} = \frac{21}{50}$

Ball not replaced

Example

There are 3 red balls and 2 green balls in a bag. One ball is chosen at random, its colour is noted and *it is not replaced*. A second ball is then chosen and its colour is also noted. Find the probability that:

(a) both balls are red

(b) both balls are the same colour

(c) at least one of the balls is green.

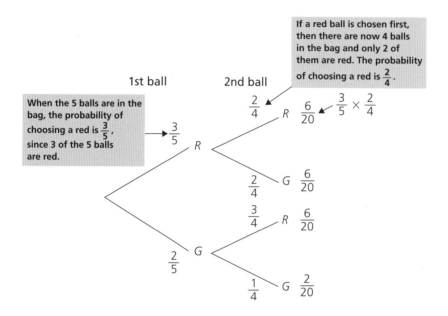

When the 5 balls are in the bag, the probability of choosing a red is $\frac{3}{5}$, since 3 of the 5 balls are red.

If a red ball is chosen first, then there are now 4 balls in the bag and only 2 of them are red. The probability of choosing a red is $\frac{2}{4}$.

(a) $P(RR) = \frac{3}{5} \times \frac{2}{4} = \frac{6}{20} = \frac{3}{10}$

(b) $P(\text{same colour}) = P(RR \text{ or } GG) = P(RR) + P(GG) = \frac{6}{20} + \frac{2}{20} = \frac{8}{20} = \frac{2}{5}$

(c) When two ball are chosen, either "At least one of the balls is green" or both of them are red.

So the probabilities of these two events add up to 1.

$P(\text{at least one } G) + P(RR) = 1$

So $P(\text{at least one } G) = 1 - P(RR)$

From the tree diagram $P(RR) = \frac{3}{10}$

And so

$P(\text{at least one } G) = 1 - P(RR)$

$\qquad\qquad\qquad\qquad = 1 - \frac{3}{10} = \frac{7}{10}$

Questions involving "at least one"
This is an example of an important short cut.
You **do not** need to think of all the cases when there is at least one green ball.

Example

60% of the population of a certain town are vaccinated against flu. The probability of someone getting flu given that they have had the vaccination is 0.2 but the probability of someone getting flu given that they have not had the vaccination is 0.65.

(a) Draw a tree diagram to represent this information.

(b) Find the probability that a person chosen at random gets flu.

(c) Write down the probability that a person chosen at random doesn't get flu given that he didn't have the vaccination.

Extended

(a)

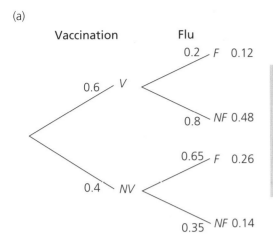

Vaccination   Flu

0.2 F 0.12

0.6 V

0.8 NF 0.48

0.65 F 0.26

0.4 NV

0.35 NF 0.14

> Notice that the probabilities on the branches that come from the same point always add up to 1.
> So
> 0.6 + 0.4 = 1
> 0.2 + 0.8 = 1
> 0.65 + 0.35 = 1

(b) There are two groups of people who get flu. Either a person has a vaccination and gets flu or a person does not have a vaccination and gets flu.

The probability that a person has a vaccination and gets flu is 0.12

The probability that a person does not have a vaccination and gets flu is 0.26

As you move **D**own a**DD** so probability of getting flu is P(F) = 0.12 + 0.26 = 0.38

(c) P(person does not get flu given he has not been vaccinated) = 0.35

(this comes straight from tree diagram)

Exam question   CIE 0580 June '08 Paper 4 Q3

(a)

Bag A   Bag B

Nadia must choose a ball from Bag A or from Bag B.

The probability that she chooses from Bag A is $\frac{2}{3}$.

Bag A contains 5 footballs and 3 tennis balls.

Bag B contains 6 footballs and 2 tennis balls.

The tree diagram below shows some of this information.

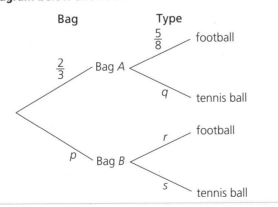

Bag   Type

$\frac{5}{8}$ football

$\frac{2}{3}$ Bag A

q tennis ball

r football

p Bag B

s tennis ball   (*Continued*)

Extended

Exam question (Continued)

    (i) **Find the values of p, q, r and s.**

    (ii) **Find the probability that Nadia chooses from Bag A and then gets a football.**

    (iii) **Find the probability that Nadia chooses a football.**

(b) **Another bag contains 7 green balls and 3 yellow balls. Sani takes three balls out of the bag, without replacement.**

    (i) **Find the probability that all three balls he chooses are yellow.**

    (ii) **Find the probability that at least one of the three balls he chooses is green.**

(a) (i) The probabilities on the branches that come from the same point always add up to 1.

$p + \frac{2}{3} = 1$ so $p = \frac{1}{3}$, $q + \frac{5}{8} = 1$ so $q = \frac{3}{8}$

In bag, B 6 of the 8 balls are footballs so $r = \frac{6}{8} = \frac{3}{4}$. It follows that $s = \frac{2}{8} = \frac{1}{4}$.

(ii) Probability of choosing bag A and then a football is $\frac{2}{3} \times \frac{5}{8} = \frac{10}{24} = \frac{5}{12}$

(iii) There are two ways of choosing a football. Either from bag A or from bag B.

P(Bag A and football) $= \frac{2}{3} \times \frac{5}{8} = \frac{10}{24} = \frac{5}{12}$

P(Bag B and football) $= \frac{1}{3} \times \frac{3}{4} = \frac{3}{12} = \frac{1}{4}$

So P(football) $= \frac{5}{12} + \frac{1}{4} = \frac{5}{12} + \frac{3}{12} = \frac{8}{12} = \frac{2}{3}$

(b) (i) Initially there are 10 balls of which 3 are yellow so the probability of the first ball being yellow is $\frac{3}{10}$.

Once a yellow ball has been taken out there are 9 balls of which 2 are yellow so the probability of the second ball being yellow is $\frac{2}{9}$.

Once a second yellow ball has been taken out there are 8 balls of which 1 is yellow so the probability of the third ball being yellow is $\frac{1}{8}$.

So the probability of all the balls being yellow is $\frac{3}{10} \times \frac{2}{9} \times \frac{1}{8} = \frac{6}{720} = \frac{1}{120}$

(ii) Either all the balls are yellow or "at least one is green". So these two events add up to 1. So P(at least one G) $= 1 - \frac{1}{120} = \frac{119}{120}$

Questions

1. The lottery basket contains 49 balls numbered from 1 to 49. What is the probability of getting:

  (a) a single digit number

  (b) an even number

  (c) a multiple of 7

  (d) a multiple of 5 or a multiple of 17?

2. A circular spinner has an arrow in the middle. The circle is split into four sections as shown in the diagram.

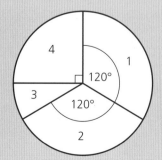

Find the probability that when the arrow is spun, the number of the section on which it lands is:

  (a) 4

  (b) 3

  (c) at least 2

  (d) an even number.

3. A circular spinner has four sections, numbered 1, 2, 3 and 4. The area for 2 is twice the area for 1, the area for 3 is three times the area for 1 and the area for 4 is four times the area for 1.

If p is the probability of getting a 1 then:

  (a) write down, in terms of p, the probabilities of getting 2, 3 and 4.

  (b) find p.

  (c) find the probability of getting an even number.

4. The probabilities associated with the scores on a biased die are shown below.

(Continued)

Questions (Continued)

Score	1	2	3	4	5	6
Probability	0.1	0.3	0.05		0.25	0.15

(a) Find the probability of getting a 4 when the die is rolled.

(b) Find the probability of getting an odd number when the die is rolled.

(c) Find the probability of getting at least 4 when the die is rolled.

5. A boy picks out a marble from a bag of 20 coloured marbles. He records its colour and then puts it back. He does this fifty times. Ten of the marbles he takes out are red. How many of the 20 marbles in the bag do you estimate to be red?

6. The spinner shown is spun 400 times. How many times would you expect the spinner to land on:

(a) the sector numbered 1

(b) a sector with an even number

(c) a sector with a number of more than 3?

7. A pack of 52 playing cards is dealt to four players so that each player gets 13 cards. This is done forty times. How many cards in total from the spades suit would one player expect to have been given from these forty deals?

8. A postman delivers letters to the Azim's house every day. The probability that he delivers them at certain times is shown below:

Time	Probability
Between 7.00 am and 7.30 am	0.15
Between 7.30 am and 8.00 am	0.3
Between 8.00 am and 8.30 am	0.35

(a) Find the probability that he delivers before 7.00 am or after 8.30 am.

It is also known that he is as likely to deliver the letters before 7.00 am as he is to deliver them after 8.30 am.

(b) Find the probability that he delivers before 7.00 am.

(c) Find the probability that he delivers a card before the Azim children go to school at 8.30 am.

(d) Find the probability that he delivers after 7.30 am.

9. A milkman always delivers the milk between 6.00 am and 9.00 am each morning. He is as likely to deliver the milk at any time in those three hours. Find the probability that he delivers the milk:

(a) before 7.00 am.

(b) between 6.15 am and 8.45 am.

Extended

10. Mr Choudry drives to work each morning. The probability that he parks his car at the front of the building is 0.4. The probability that he parks his car at the side of the building is 0.15. The rest of the time he parks at the back of the building.

(a) What is the probability that he will park at the back of the building on any particular morning?

(b) What is the probability that he will park either at the back or at the side of the building on any particular morning?

(c) In the next year, he works for 220 days. On approximately how many days will Mr Choudry park either at the back or at the side of the building?

11. The probability that Ayesha is late for school is 0.4 and the probability that Leena is late is 0.7.

(a) What assumption do you need to make to calculate the probability that both girls are late for school?

(b) Making this assumption, draw a tree diagram to show all the possibilities.

(c) Calculate the probability that both girls are late for school.

(d) Calculate also the probability that only one of the two girls is late for school.

12. A box contains 12 counters of which 2 are blue, 3 are red and the rest are purple. Two counters are chosen at random, the first being replaced before the second is chosen.

Find the probability that

(a) the first counter is purple and the second is blue

(b) both counters are red

(c) one of the counters is blue and the other is red.

13. Three coins are tossed at the same time.

(a) List all the eight possible outcomes, using *H* and *T*.

(b) Find the probability of

(i) getting three tails

(ii) getting the same outcome on all three coins

(iii) getting two heads and one tail (in any order)

(iv) *not* getting three heads.

14. A coin is biased so that the head appears twice as often as the tail.

(Continued)

Extended

Questions (*Continued*)

(a) If p is the probability of getting a tail, write down the probability of getting a head in terms of p.

(b) Hence show that $p = \frac{1}{3}$.

(c) The coin is tossed twice. Find the probability of getting
   (i) two heads
   (ii) a head first and then a tail
   (iii) two tails.

15. (a) Without listing them, write down how many possible outcomes there are when six coins are tossed together.

(b) What is the probability of tossing six heads?

16. Five yellow balls and three red balls are placed in a bag and two are removed, one at a time, without replacement.

(a) Draw a tree diagram to represent the above information.

(b) Find the probability that
   (i) both balls are red
   (ii) both balls are the same colour
   (iii) the second ball is yellow given that the first is red.

17. A boy is late 60% of the time when it is raining and 30% of the time when it is dry. It rains on 25% of days.

(a) Draw a tree diagram to represent the above information.

(b) Find the probability that
   (i) it is raining and he is late
   (ii) he is late
   (iii) he is on time given that it is dry.

18. A fair coin is tossed twenty times. Given that the coin shows heads each time what is the probability of the coin showing heads on the next toss?

34 Vectors

If the point A (−3, 2) is translated to the point B (−1, 5) then A moves 2 units to the right and 3 units up. The translation can be represented by the column vector $\begin{pmatrix} 2 \\ 3 \end{pmatrix}$.

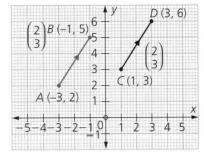

The notation $\overrightarrow{AB}$ is used to describe the translation from A to B.

So in this example $\overrightarrow{AB} = \begin{pmatrix} 2 \\ 3 \end{pmatrix}$.

The same translation moves the point C (1, 3) to D (3, 6).

The notation $\overrightarrow{CD}$ is used to describe the translation from C to D. So $\overrightarrow{CD} = \begin{pmatrix} 2 \\ 3 \end{pmatrix}$.

So $\overrightarrow{AB} = \overrightarrow{CD}$.

The two vectors $\overrightarrow{AB}$ and $\overrightarrow{CD}$ have the same direction and the same length.

The vector $\begin{pmatrix} -2 \\ -3 \end{pmatrix}$ will translate B back to A.

A vector can also be represented by a small case letter. In text books these are printed in bold, for example $\mathbf{a} = \begin{pmatrix} 2 \\ 3 \end{pmatrix}$ and $\mathbf{b} = \begin{pmatrix} 4 \\ 1 \end{pmatrix}$. Such vectors should be *underlined when written by hand*.

Position vectors

The position vector of a point A tells you the position of A relative to the origin.

So the position vector of the point A (−3, 2) is the vector $\overrightarrow{OA} = \begin{pmatrix} -3 \\ 2 \end{pmatrix}$.

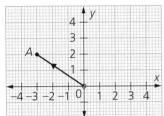

Parallel vectors

Parallel vectors have the same direction.

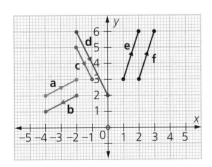

$$\mathbf{a} = \begin{pmatrix} 2 \\ 1 \end{pmatrix} \qquad \mathbf{b} = \begin{pmatrix} -2 \\ -1 \end{pmatrix}$$

$$\mathbf{c} = \begin{pmatrix} 1 \\ -2 \end{pmatrix} \qquad \mathbf{d} = \begin{pmatrix} 2 \\ -4 \end{pmatrix}$$

$$\mathbf{e} = \begin{pmatrix} 1 \\ 3 \end{pmatrix} \qquad \mathbf{f} = \begin{pmatrix} 1 \\ 3 \end{pmatrix}$$

$\mathbf{e} = \mathbf{f}$ $\mathbf{e}$ and $\mathbf{f}$ are equal in length and have the same direction.

$\mathbf{a} = -\mathbf{b}$ $\mathbf{a}$ and $\mathbf{b}$ are equal in length but have opposite directions.

$\mathbf{d} = 2\mathbf{c}$ $\mathbf{d}$ and $\mathbf{c}$ have the same direction but the length of $\mathbf{d}$ is twice the length of $\mathbf{c}$.

If two vectors are parallel both the corresponding components will be in the same ratio.

Example

$\overrightarrow{AB} = \begin{pmatrix} 1 \\ -2 \end{pmatrix}$ and $\overrightarrow{CD} = 4\overrightarrow{AB}$.

(a) Write $\overrightarrow{CD}$ as a column vector.

(b) What can you say about $\overrightarrow{AB}$ and $\overrightarrow{CD}$?

(a) $\overrightarrow{CD} = 4\begin{pmatrix} 1 \\ -2 \end{pmatrix} = \begin{pmatrix} 4 \\ -8 \end{pmatrix}$

(b) $\overrightarrow{AB}$ and $\overrightarrow{CD}$ are parallel.
$\overrightarrow{CD}$ is four times as long as $\overrightarrow{AB}$.

Adding and subtracting vectors

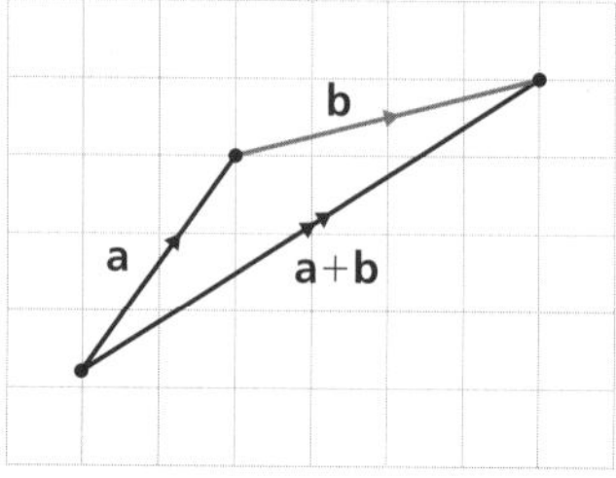

Example

If $\mathbf{a} = \begin{pmatrix} 2 \\ 3 \end{pmatrix}$ and $\mathbf{b} = \begin{pmatrix} 4 \\ 1 \end{pmatrix}$ write the following as column vectors:

(a) a + b

(b) a − b

(a) $\mathbf{a} + \mathbf{b} = \begin{pmatrix} 2 \\ 3 \end{pmatrix} + \begin{pmatrix} 4 \\ 1 \end{pmatrix} = \begin{pmatrix} 6 \\ 4 \end{pmatrix}$

To add column vectors add their corresponding components.

(b) $\mathbf{a} - \mathbf{b} = \mathbf{a} + (-\mathbf{b}) = \begin{pmatrix} 2 \\ 3 \end{pmatrix} + \begin{pmatrix} -4 \\ -1 \end{pmatrix} = \begin{pmatrix} -2 \\ 2 \end{pmatrix}$

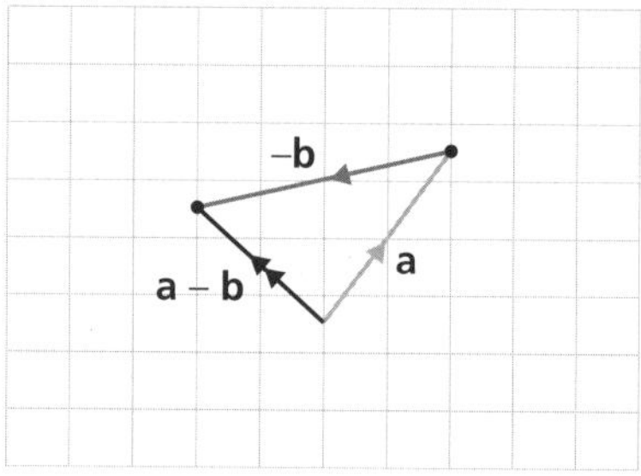

Multiplying a vector by a scalar

Example

If $\mathbf{a} = \begin{pmatrix} 2 \\ 3 \end{pmatrix}$ and $\mathbf{b} = \begin{pmatrix} 4 \\ 1 \end{pmatrix}$ write as column vectors:

(a) 5a

(b) 3a + 2b

(a) $5\mathbf{a} = \begin{pmatrix} 5 \times 2 \\ 5 \times 3 \end{pmatrix} = \begin{pmatrix} 10 \\ 15 \end{pmatrix}$

Multiply each component by the scalar, 5.

(b) $3\mathbf{a} + 2\mathbf{b} = 3\begin{pmatrix} 2 \\ 3 \end{pmatrix} + 2\begin{pmatrix} 4 \\ 1 \end{pmatrix}$

$= \begin{pmatrix} 6 \\ 9 \end{pmatrix} + \begin{pmatrix} 8 \\ 2 \end{pmatrix}$

$= \begin{pmatrix} 14 \\ 11 \end{pmatrix}$

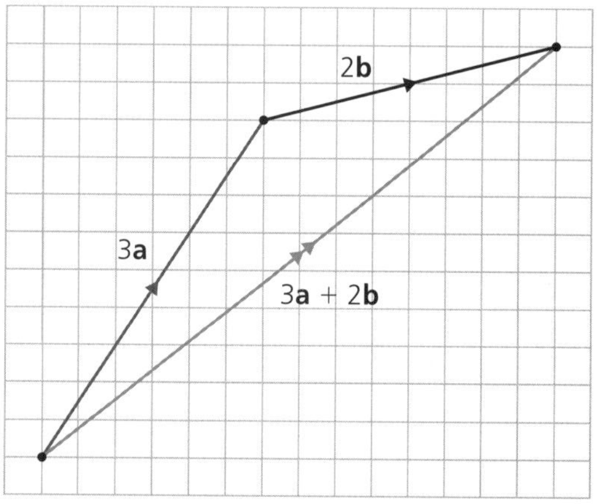

Extended

Magnitude of a vector

The **magnitude** of a vector is its length.

The magnitude of a vector **a** is written $|\mathbf{a}|$.

If $\overrightarrow{AB} = \begin{pmatrix} 2 \\ 3 \end{pmatrix} = \mathbf{a}$ you can find $|\mathbf{a}|$ by using Pythagoras' theorem.

$AB^2 = 2^2 + 3^2$

$= 4 + 9$

$= 13$

$AB = \sqrt{13} = 3.61$ to 3 sf

so $|\mathbf{a}| = 3.61$

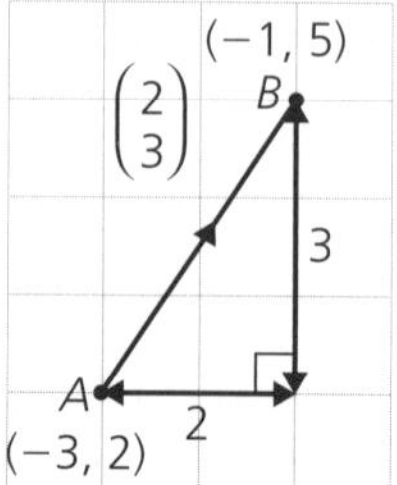

Example

Find the magnitude of the vector a + b where a = $\begin{pmatrix} 3 \\ 2 \end{pmatrix}$ and b = $\begin{pmatrix} 7 \\ 5 \end{pmatrix}$.

$$\mathbf{a} + \mathbf{b} = \begin{pmatrix} 3 \\ 2 \end{pmatrix} + \begin{pmatrix} 7 \\ 5 \end{pmatrix} = \begin{pmatrix} 10 \\ 7 \end{pmatrix}$$

$$|\mathbf{a} + \mathbf{b}| = \sqrt{10^2 + 7^2} = 149 = 12.2 \text{ to 3 sf}$$

Vector geometry

$ABCD$ is a parallelogram in which $\overrightarrow{DC} = \mathbf{u}$ and $\overrightarrow{AD} = \mathbf{v}$.

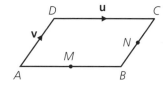

$$\overrightarrow{DA} = -\overrightarrow{AD} = -\mathbf{v}$$

Since $ABCD$ is a parallelogram $\overrightarrow{AB} = \mathbf{u}$ and $\overrightarrow{BC} = \mathbf{v}$.

M is the midpoint of AB and N is the midpoint of BC so

$$\overrightarrow{AM} = \overrightarrow{MB} = \frac{1}{2}\mathbf{u} \text{ and } \overrightarrow{BN} = \overrightarrow{NC} = \frac{1}{2}\mathbf{v}.$$

A translation from A to D and then from D to C is equivalent to a translation from A to C. This can be expressed in vectors as follows:

$$\overrightarrow{AD} + \overrightarrow{DC} = \overrightarrow{AC}$$

Since $\overrightarrow{AD} = \mathbf{v}$ and $\overrightarrow{DC} = \mathbf{u}$, it follows that $\overrightarrow{AC} = \mathbf{u} + \mathbf{v}$

A translation from D to C and then from C to N is equivalent to a translation from D to N. This can be expressed in vectors as follows:

$$\overrightarrow{DC} + \overrightarrow{CN} = \overrightarrow{DN}$$

Since $\overrightarrow{DC} = \mathbf{u}$ and $\overrightarrow{CN} = -\overrightarrow{NC} = -\frac{1}{2}\mathbf{v}$, it follows that $\overrightarrow{DN} = \mathbf{u} - \frac{1}{2}\mathbf{v}$

A translation from M to B and then from B to N is equivalent to a translation from M to N. This can be expressed in vectors as follows:

$$\overrightarrow{MB} + \overrightarrow{BN} = \overrightarrow{MN}$$

Since $\overrightarrow{MB} = \frac{1}{2}\mathbf{u}$ and $\overrightarrow{BN} = \frac{1}{2}\mathbf{v}$, it follows that $\overrightarrow{MN} = \frac{1}{2}\mathbf{u} + \frac{1}{2}\mathbf{v}$

Notice that $\overrightarrow{MN} = \frac{1}{2}\mathbf{u} + \frac{1}{2}\mathbf{v} = \frac{1}{2}(\mathbf{u} + \mathbf{v}) = \frac{1}{2}\overrightarrow{AC}$

This means that MN is parallel to AC and that MN is half the length of AC.

Example

X is the midpoint of AB and Y is the midpoint of BC.

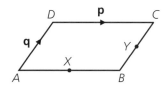

(a) Find the following in terms of p and q:

    (i) $\overrightarrow{XB}$

   (ii) $\overrightarrow{BY}$

  (iii) $\overrightarrow{XY}$

(b) What can you say about *XY* and *AC*?

(a) (i) $\overrightarrow{XB} = \frac{1}{2}\mathbf{p}$

   (ii) $\overrightarrow{BY} = \frac{1}{2}\mathbf{q}$

   (iii) Hence $\overrightarrow{XY} = \overrightarrow{XB} + \overrightarrow{BY} = \frac{1}{2}\mathbf{p} + \frac{1}{2}\mathbf{q}$

(b) $\overrightarrow{AC} = \overrightarrow{AB} + \overrightarrow{BC} = \mathbf{p} + \mathbf{q}$

   $\overrightarrow{XY} = \frac{1}{2}\mathbf{p} + \frac{1}{2}\mathbf{q} = \frac{1}{2}(\mathbf{p} + \mathbf{q}) = \frac{1}{2}\overrightarrow{AC}$

Hence *XY* and *AC* are parallel and *XY* is half *AC*.

Exam question

CIE 0580 November '06 Paper 4 Q6 a and b

(a)

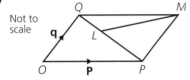

Not to scale

OPMQ is a parallelogram and *O* is the origin.
$\overrightarrow{OP} = p$ and $\overrightarrow{OQ} = q$.
L is on *PQ* so that *PL : LQ* = 2:1.

Find the following vectors in terms of p and q. Write your answers in their simplest form.
  (i) $\overrightarrow{PQ}$
  (ii) $\overrightarrow{PL}$
  (iii) $\overrightarrow{ML}$
  (iv) the position vector of *L*.

(b) *R* is the point (1, 2). It is translated to the point *S* by the vector $\begin{pmatrix} 3 \\ -4 \end{pmatrix}$.
  (i) Write down the coordinates of *S*.
  (ii) Write down the vector which translates *S* onto *R*.

(a) (i) $\overrightarrow{PQ} = \overrightarrow{PO} + \overrightarrow{OQ} = -\mathbf{p} + \mathbf{q}$

   (ii) $\overrightarrow{PL} = \frac{2}{3}\overrightarrow{PQ} = -\frac{2}{3}\mathbf{p} + \frac{2}{3}\mathbf{q}$

   (iii) $\overrightarrow{ML} = \overrightarrow{MP} + \overrightarrow{PL} = -\mathbf{q} + \left(-\frac{2}{3}\mathbf{p} + \frac{2}{3}\mathbf{q}\right) = -\frac{2}{3}\mathbf{p} - \frac{1}{3}\mathbf{q}$

   (iv) $\overrightarrow{OL} = \overrightarrow{OP} + \overrightarrow{PL} = \mathbf{p} + \left(-\frac{2}{3}\mathbf{p} + \frac{2}{3}\mathbf{q}\right) = \frac{1}{3}\mathbf{p} + \frac{2}{3}\mathbf{q}$

(b) (i) Coordinates of *S* are (1 + 3, 2 − 4) = (4, −2).

   (ii) $\begin{pmatrix} 3 \\ -4 \end{pmatrix}$ translates *R* onto *S* so the vector $\begin{pmatrix} -3 \\ 4 \end{pmatrix}$ translates *S* onto *R*.

Exam question

CIE 0580 June '08 Paper 4 Q9

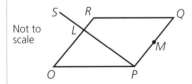

Not to scale

OPQR is a parallelogram.
O is the origin.
$\overrightarrow{OP} = p$ and $\overrightarrow{OR} = r$.
M is the midpoint of *PQ* and *L* is on *OR* such that *OL : LR* = 2 : 1.
The line *PL* is extended to the point *S*.

(Continued)

Exam question (Continued)

(a) Find, in terms of p and r, in their simplest forms,

- (i) $\overrightarrow{OQ}$
- (ii) $\overrightarrow{PR}$
- (iii) $\overrightarrow{PL}$
- (iv) the position vector of M.

(b) PLS is a straight line and $PS = \frac{3}{2} PL$.

Find, in terms of p and/or r, in their simplest forms,

- (i) $\overrightarrow{PS}$
- (ii) $\overrightarrow{QS}$

(c) What can you say about the points Q, R and S?

$OPQR$ is a parallelogram, $\overrightarrow{PQ} = \overrightarrow{OR} = \mathbf{r}$ and $\overrightarrow{RQ} = \overrightarrow{OP} = \mathbf{p}$

(a) (i) $\overrightarrow{OQ} = \overrightarrow{OP} + \overrightarrow{PQ} = \mathbf{p} + \mathbf{r}$

(ii) $\overrightarrow{PR} = \overrightarrow{PO} + \overrightarrow{OR} = -\mathbf{p} + \mathbf{r}$

(iii) Since $OL : LR$ is $2 : 1$ it follows that $\overrightarrow{OL} = \frac{2}{3} \overrightarrow{OR} = \frac{2}{3} \mathbf{r}$

$\overrightarrow{PL} = \overrightarrow{PO} + \overrightarrow{OL} = -\mathbf{p} + \frac{2}{3} \mathbf{r}$

(iv) Since M is the midpoint of PQ it follows that $\overrightarrow{PM} = \frac{1}{2} PQ = \frac{1}{2} \mathbf{r}$

Position vector of M is $\overrightarrow{OM} = \overrightarrow{OP} + \overrightarrow{PM} = \mathbf{p} + \frac{1}{2} \mathbf{r}$

(b) (i) $\overrightarrow{PS} = \frac{3}{2} \overrightarrow{PL} = \frac{3}{2} (-\mathbf{p} + \frac{2}{3} \mathbf{r})$ using (a) (iii)

So $\overrightarrow{PS} = -\frac{3}{2} \mathbf{p} + \mathbf{r}$

(ii) $\overrightarrow{QS} = \overrightarrow{QP} + \overrightarrow{PS} = -\mathbf{r} + (-\frac{3}{2} \mathbf{p} + \mathbf{r}) = -\frac{3}{2} \mathbf{p}$

(c) Since $\overrightarrow{QR} = -\mathbf{p}$ and $\overrightarrow{QS} = -\frac{3}{2} \mathbf{p}$ it follows that $\overrightarrow{QS} = \frac{3}{2} \overrightarrow{QR}$.

This shows that Q, R and S all lie on a straight line.

> This is an example of an important result:
> If you can show that any two of the vectors $\overrightarrow{AB}$, $\overrightarrow{AC}$ and $\overrightarrow{BC}$ are parallel then the three points A, B and C lie on a straight line.

Questions

1. If $\mathbf{a} = \begin{pmatrix} 1 \\ 7 \end{pmatrix}$ and $\mathbf{b} = \begin{pmatrix} -2 \\ 3 \end{pmatrix}$ write these as column vectors:

- (a) $2\mathbf{a}$
- (b) $\mathbf{a} + \mathbf{b}$
- (c) $\mathbf{a} - \mathbf{b}$
- (d) $3\mathbf{a} + 4\mathbf{b}$

2. $ABCD$ is a parallelogram such that $\overrightarrow{AB} = \mathbf{p}$ and $\overrightarrow{BC} = \mathbf{q}$. Find these vectors in terms of $\mathbf{p}$ and $\mathbf{q}$:

- (a) $\overrightarrow{CD}$
- (b) $\overrightarrow{AD}$
- (c) $\overrightarrow{AC}$
- (d) $\overrightarrow{AM}$ where M is the midpoint of AB
- (e) $\overrightarrow{AN}$ where N is the midpoint of AC
- (f) $\overrightarrow{AP}$ where P is the point along AC which is twice as far from A as from C (P is between A and C).

3. $ABCD$ is a parallelogram (labelled anticlockwise) with $\overrightarrow{AB} = \mathbf{p}$ and $\overrightarrow{AD} = \mathbf{q}$. M is the midpoint of AD, N is the midpoint of AB and R is one-quarter of the way along AC from A.

(a) Find the following in terms of $\mathbf{p}$ and $\mathbf{q}$ (in the form __ $\mathbf{p}$ + __ $\mathbf{q}$):

- (i) $\overrightarrow{AM}$
- (ii) $\overrightarrow{AN}$
- (iii) $\overrightarrow{AC}$
- (iv) $\overrightarrow{AR}$
- (v) $\overrightarrow{MR}$
- (vi) $\overrightarrow{RN}$

(b) Hence show that M, N and R all lie on a straight line (by showing that MR is parallel to RN).

(c) Find the ratio $MR : MN$.

4. ABC is a triangle (labelled anticlockwise) with $\overrightarrow{AB} = \mathbf{p}$ and $\overrightarrow{AC} = \mathbf{q}$. X, Y and Z are the midpoint of AB, BC and CA respectively.

(a) Find the following in terms of $\mathbf{p}$ and $\mathbf{q}$ (in the form __ $\mathbf{p}$ + __ $\mathbf{q}$):

- (i) $\overrightarrow{BC}$
- (ii) $\overrightarrow{BY}$
- (iii) $\overrightarrow{XB}$
- (iv) $\overrightarrow{XY}$
- (v) $\overrightarrow{YC}$
- (vi) $\overrightarrow{YZ}$
- (vii) $\overrightarrow{AZ}$
- (viii) $\overrightarrow{XZ}$

(b) Hence show that XZ is parallel to BC.

(c) Find the ratio $XZ : BC$.

5. $ABCD$ is a parallelogram (labelled anticlockwise) with $\overrightarrow{AB} = \mathbf{r}$ and $\overrightarrow{AD} = \mathbf{s}$. X is two-thirds of the way along BD from B and Y is one-third of the way along AD from A.

(a) Find the following in terms of $\mathbf{r}$ and $\mathbf{s}$ (in the form __ $\mathbf{r}$ + __ $\mathbf{s}$):

- (i) $\overrightarrow{BD}$
- (ii) $\overrightarrow{AC}$
- (iii) $\overrightarrow{BX}$
- (iv) $\overrightarrow{AX}$
- (v) $\overrightarrow{AY}$
- (vi) $\overrightarrow{YX}$

(b) Hence show that YX is parallel to AC.

(c) Find the ratio $YX : AC$.

35 Matrices

The matrix $\mathbf{A} = \begin{pmatrix} 7 & 2 & 9 \\ 6 & 8 & 1 \end{pmatrix}$ 2 rows has 2 rows and 3 columns so it is a 2×3 matrix.

3 columns

2×3 is the **order** of the matrix.

A has 6 elements and the element 9 is in the first row and the third column.

> Order is **RC**
> rows × columns

Adding matrices

Example

If $\mathbf{A} = \begin{pmatrix} 2 & 3 & 7 \\ 5 & 1 & 4 \end{pmatrix}$ and $\mathbf{B} = \begin{pmatrix} 6 & 5 & 8 \\ 9 & 3 & 1 \end{pmatrix}$ find $\mathbf{A} + \mathbf{B}$.

$\mathbf{A} + \mathbf{B} = \begin{pmatrix} 2 & 3 & 7 \\ 5 & 1 & 4 \end{pmatrix} + \begin{pmatrix} 6 & 5 & 8 \\ 9 & 3 & 1 \end{pmatrix}$

$= \begin{pmatrix} 2+6 & 3+5 & 7+8 \\ 5+9 & 1+3 & 4+1 \end{pmatrix}$

$= \begin{pmatrix} 8 & 8 & 15 \\ 14 & 4 & 5 \end{pmatrix}$

> You can only add matrices that have the same order.
> **A** is 2×3 and **B** is 2×3

Multiplying matrices

If $\mathbf{A} = \begin{pmatrix} a & b \\ c & d \end{pmatrix}$ and $\mathbf{B} = \begin{pmatrix} p & q & t \\ r & t & u \end{pmatrix}$ then **AB** is called the product of **A** and **B**.

order $2 \times \mathbf{2}$ $\qquad \mathbf{2} \times 3$

A has **2** columns and **B** has **2** rows.

To find **AB** you multiply the elements in the first **row** of **A** by the corresponding elements in the first **column** of **B**.

$\begin{pmatrix} a & b \\ \ldots & \ldots \end{pmatrix} \begin{pmatrix} p & \ldots \\ q & \ldots \end{pmatrix} = \begin{pmatrix} ap + bq & \ldots \\ \ldots & \ldots \end{pmatrix}$

Following this pattern to find the other entries gives:

$\mathbf{AB} = \begin{pmatrix} a & b \\ c & d \end{pmatrix} \begin{pmatrix} p & q & t \\ r & s & u \end{pmatrix} = \begin{pmatrix} ap + br & aq + bs & at + bu \\ cp + dr & cq + ds & ct + du \end{pmatrix}$

You can only multiply matrices if they are **compatible**, that is if the number of **columns** in the left-hand matrix is the same as the number of **rows** in the right-hand matrix.
Write the order under each matrix. If the two inside numbers are equal you can multiply the matrices. The order of the final matrix comes from the outside numbers.

Example

If $\mathbf{A} = \begin{pmatrix} 3 & 4 \\ 2 & 5 \\ 1 & 6 \end{pmatrix}$ and $\mathbf{B} = \begin{pmatrix} 7 & 8 & 6 & 5 \\ 2 & 1 & 4 & 9 \end{pmatrix}$ then find AB.

$\quad 3 \times 2 \qquad\qquad 2 \times 4$

> **Inside numbers are equal**

$\mathbf{AB} = \begin{pmatrix} 3 & 4 \\ 2 & 5 \\ 1 & 6 \end{pmatrix} \begin{pmatrix} 7 & 8 & 6 & 5 \\ 2 & 1 & 4 & 9 \end{pmatrix} = \begin{pmatrix} 3\times7+4\times2 & 3\times8+4\times1 & 3\times6+4\times4 & 3\times5+4\times9 \\ 2\times7+5\times2 & 2\times8+5\times1 & 2\times6+5\times4 & 2\times5+5\times9 \\ 1\times7+6\times2 & 1\times8+6\times1 & 1\times6+6\times4 & 1\times5+6\times9 \end{pmatrix}$

$= \begin{pmatrix} 29 & 28 & 34 & 51 \\ 24 & 21 & 32 & 55 \\ 19 & 14 & 30 & 59 \end{pmatrix}$

$\qquad 3 \times 4$

> **Order of AB comes from outside numbers**

Example

If $A = \begin{pmatrix} 2 & 3 \\ 1 & 7 \end{pmatrix}$ and $B = \begin{pmatrix} 4 & 5 \\ -3 & 2 \end{pmatrix}$ then find AB and BA.

2×2 2×2

$AB = \begin{pmatrix} 2 & 3 \\ 1 & 7 \end{pmatrix} \begin{pmatrix} 4 & 5 \\ -3 & 2 \end{pmatrix}$

$= \begin{pmatrix} 2 \times 4 + 3 \times -3 & 2 \times 5 + 3 \times 2 \\ 1 \times 4 + 7 \times -3 & 1 \times 5 + 7 \times 2 \end{pmatrix}$

$= \begin{pmatrix} -1 & 16 \\ -17 & 19 \end{pmatrix}$

$BA = \begin{pmatrix} 4 & 5 \\ -3 & 2 \end{pmatrix} \begin{pmatrix} 2 & 3 \\ 1 & 7 \end{pmatrix}$

$= \begin{pmatrix} 4 \times 2 + 5 \times 1 & 4 \times 3 + 5 \times 7 \\ -3 \times 2 + 2 \times 1 & -3 \times 3 + 2 \times 7 \end{pmatrix}$

$= \begin{pmatrix} 13 & 47 \\ -4 & 5 \end{pmatrix}$

In general, AB is not the same as BA

Example

Find AB if $A = (3 \quad 7)$ and $B = \begin{pmatrix} 5 \\ 3 \end{pmatrix}$.

$AB = (3 \quad 7) \begin{pmatrix} 5 \\ 3 \end{pmatrix} = (3 \times 5 + 7 \times 3) = (36)$

order 1×2 2×1 1×1

The identity matrix

The matrix $I = \begin{pmatrix} 1 & 0 \\ 0 & 1 \end{pmatrix}$ is the identity matrix.

$IA = AI = A$ for all 2×2 matrices A.

The matrix I leaves all 2×2 matrices unchanged.

For example $\begin{pmatrix} 1 & 0 \\ 0 & 1 \end{pmatrix} \begin{pmatrix} -2 & 1 \\ 4 & 3 \end{pmatrix} = \begin{pmatrix} -2 & 1 \\ 4 & 3 \end{pmatrix}$ and $\begin{pmatrix} -2 & 1 \\ 4 & 3 \end{pmatrix} \begin{pmatrix} 1 & 0 \\ 0 & 1 \end{pmatrix} = \begin{pmatrix} -2 & 1 \\ 4 & 3 \end{pmatrix}$

The determinant

If $A = \begin{pmatrix} a & b \\ c & d \end{pmatrix}$ then the determinant of A is det $A = ad - bc$. It is also denoted by $|A|$ or $\begin{vmatrix} a & b \\ c & d \end{vmatrix}$.

* A matrix is said to be **singular** if the determinant is zero.
* A matrix is said to be **non-singular** if the determinant is not zero.

Inverses

The inverse of the matrix A is given by $A^{-1} = \dfrac{1}{ad - bc} \begin{pmatrix} d & -b \\ -c & a \end{pmatrix}$.

You can only find the inverse of A when A is non-singular.

The transformation represented by A^{-1}, the inverse matrix, is the inverse of the transformation represented by A.

So if $A = \begin{pmatrix} 2 & 3 \\ 1 & 7 \end{pmatrix}$ then $A^{-1} = \dfrac{1}{2 \times 7 - 1 \times 3} \begin{pmatrix} 7 & -3 \\ -1 & 2 \end{pmatrix} = \dfrac{1}{11} \begin{pmatrix} 7 & -3 \\ -1 & 2 \end{pmatrix}$.

and $AA^{-1} = \dfrac{1}{11} \begin{pmatrix} 2 & 3 \\ 1 & 7 \end{pmatrix} \begin{pmatrix} 7 & -3 \\ -1 & 2 \end{pmatrix} = \dfrac{1}{11} \begin{pmatrix} 11 & 0 \\ 0 & 11 \end{pmatrix} = \begin{pmatrix} 1 & 0 \\ 0 & 1 \end{pmatrix}$

Similarly if $B = \begin{pmatrix} 4 & 5 \\ -3 & 2 \end{pmatrix}$ then $B^{-1} = \dfrac{1}{4 \times 2 - 3 \times (-5)} \begin{pmatrix} 2 & -5 \\ 3 & 4 \end{pmatrix} = \dfrac{1}{23} \begin{pmatrix} 2 & -5 \\ 3 & 4 \end{pmatrix}$.

and $BB^{-1} = \dfrac{1}{23} \begin{pmatrix} 4 & 5 \\ -3 & 2 \end{pmatrix} \begin{pmatrix} 2 & -5 \\ 3 & 4 \end{pmatrix} = \dfrac{1}{23} \begin{pmatrix} 23 & 0 \\ 0 & 23 \end{pmatrix} = \begin{pmatrix} 1 & 0 \\ 0 & 1 \end{pmatrix}$

The identity matrix $\mathbf{I} = \begin{pmatrix} 1 & 0 \\ 0 & 1 \end{pmatrix}$ is such that $\mathbf{AI} = \mathbf{A} = \mathbf{IA}$ for all 2×2 matrices $\mathbf{A}$.

It follows from this that $\mathbf{A}^{-1}\mathbf{A} = \mathbf{I} = \mathbf{AA}^{-1}$.

Example

Find the inverse of the matrix $\mathbf{A} = \begin{pmatrix} 3 & 2 \\ -1 & 4 \end{pmatrix}$.

$\det \mathbf{A} = 3 \times 4 - 2 \times (-1) = 14$

So $\mathbf{A}^{-1} = \dfrac{1}{14}\begin{pmatrix} 4 & -2 \\ 1 & 3 \end{pmatrix}$

Exam question CIE 0580 November '06 Paper 2 Q19

(a) Find $(3 \quad 4)\begin{pmatrix} 5 \\ 2 \end{pmatrix}$.

(b) $\begin{pmatrix} 7 \\ 3 \end{pmatrix}(x \quad y) = \begin{pmatrix} 28 & 42 \\ 12 & 18 \end{pmatrix}$. **Find the values of** x **and** y.

(c) **Explain why** $\begin{pmatrix} 15 & 20 \\ 6 & 8 \end{pmatrix}$ **does not have an inverse.**

(a) $(3 \quad 4)\begin{pmatrix} 5 \\ 2 \end{pmatrix} = (23)$

$1 \times 2 \quad 2 \times 1 \quad 1 \times 1$

(b) $\begin{pmatrix} 7 \\ 3 \end{pmatrix} \quad (x \quad y) = \begin{pmatrix} 7x & 7y \\ 3x & 3y \end{pmatrix}$

$2 \times 1 \quad 1 \times 2 \qquad 2 \times 2$

Solving $\begin{pmatrix} 7x & 7y \\ 3x & 3y \end{pmatrix} = \begin{pmatrix} 28 & 42 \\ 12 & 18 \end{pmatrix}$ gives $x = 4$ and $y = 6$.

(c) $\det\begin{pmatrix} 15 & 20 \\ 6 & 8 \end{pmatrix} = 120 - 120 = 0$.

So $\begin{pmatrix} 15 & 20 \\ 6 & 8 \end{pmatrix}$ is a singular matrix and does not have an inverse.

Questions

1. If $\begin{pmatrix} x & 1 \\ 5 & z \end{pmatrix} + \begin{pmatrix} -3 & 3 \\ y & 3 \end{pmatrix} = \begin{pmatrix} y & z \\ z & 7 \end{pmatrix}$, find x, y, and z.

2. If $\mathbf{A} = \begin{pmatrix} 3 & 7 \\ 2 & 5 \end{pmatrix}$, $\mathbf{B} = \begin{pmatrix} 4 & 11 \\ 3 & 8 \end{pmatrix}$ and $\mathbf{C} = \begin{pmatrix} 3 & 4 \\ 7 & 9 \end{pmatrix}$ find the

following:

(a) $\mathbf{A} + \mathbf{B}$ (b) $\mathbf{A} - 2\mathbf{B}$

(c) $5\mathbf{C} - 2\mathbf{A}$ (d) $\mathbf{AB}$

(e) $\mathbf{BA}$ (f) $\mathbf{CB}$

3. $\mathbf{A} = \begin{pmatrix} 5 & 2 \\ 10 & x \end{pmatrix}$

(a) Find the value of x for which $\mathbf{A}$ does not have an inverse.

(b) Find $\mathbf{A}^{-1}$ when $x = 6$.

4. Find x and y if

$\begin{pmatrix} 2 \\ 3 \end{pmatrix}(x \quad 5) = \begin{pmatrix} 14 & 10 \\ y & 15 \end{pmatrix}$

5. If $\mathbf{A} = \begin{pmatrix} 5 & 6 \\ 2 & 4 \end{pmatrix}$ and $\mathbf{B} = \begin{pmatrix} 3 & 4 \\ 7 & 9 \end{pmatrix}$ then find:

(a) $\mathbf{A}^{-1}$ (b) $\mathbf{B}^{-1}$

(c) $\mathbf{B}^{-1}\mathbf{A}^{-1}$ (d) $\mathbf{A}^{-1}\mathbf{B}^{-1}$

(e) $(\mathbf{AB})^{-1}$ (f) $(\mathbf{BA})^{-1}$

6. If $\mathbf{A} = \begin{pmatrix} 1 & 0 \\ 3 & 2 \end{pmatrix}$ and $\mathbf{B} = \begin{pmatrix} x & 0 \\ 1 & 3 \end{pmatrix}$ and $\mathbf{AB} = \mathbf{BA}$ find x.

36 Transformations

A transformation moves a shape from one position to another.
You can transform a shape by **reflecting** (as in a mirror), **rotating** (turning), **translating** (moving) or **enlarging** it.

The shape you start with is called the **object** and the shape you end with is called the **image**.

In a reflection, rotation or translation the object and image are **congruent**, that is, they are the same shape and size.

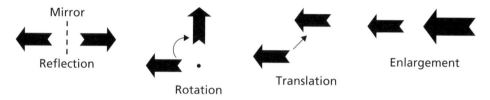

Reflections

You describe a reflection by naming the mirror line.

Triangle *B* is a reflection of triangle *A* in the line $x = 1$.

Triangle *A* is the object.
Triangle *B* is the image.

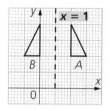

> Notice that the distance from triangle *A* to the mirror line is the same as the distance from triangle *B* to the mirror line.

Example

Draw axes labelled from −3 to 3.
The triangle *ABC* has vertices at *A* (−1, 1), *B* (0, 1) and *C* (1, 3).
The transformation M is a reflection in the line $y = x$.
Draw M (*ABC*), the image of triangle *ABC* under M.

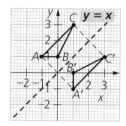

> Notice that the lines joining each vertex to its image is perpendicular to the mirror line $y = x$.
> When (*p*, *q*) is reflected in the line $y = x$ its image is (*q*, *p*)

Rotations

You describe a rotation by naming the **centre**, the **angle** and the **direction** (clockwise or anticlockwise) of the rotation.

The diagram shows an L-shape rotated through angles of 90°, 180° and 270° about a fixed point.

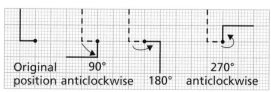

Original   90°   270°
position   anticlockwise   180°   anticlockwise

Example

Find the image of the triangle with vertices A (2, 2), B (4, 5) and C (6, 3) when it is rotated by 90°anticlockwise about X (0, 4).

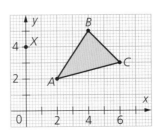

The simplest way to do this is to imagine L-shapes joining (0, 4) to the three vertices and then rotate these Ls as shown in the diagrams.

A (2, 2) gets mapped to (2, 6)   *B* (4, 5) gets mapped to (−1, 8)   *C* (6, 3) gets mapped to (1, 10).

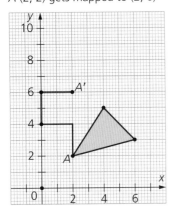   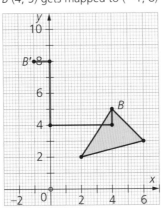   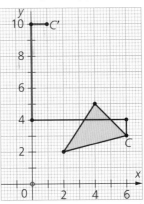

The diagram shows triangle *ABC* and its image *A' B' C'*.

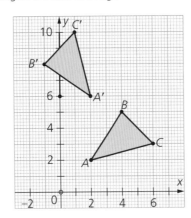

Translations

You describe a translation with a **vector**.

Triangle *A* is translated to triangle *B* by the vector $\binom{2}{1}$.

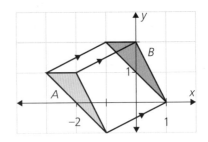

- The top number in the vector tells you the horizontal movement (positive right, negative left).
- The bottom number in the vector tells you the vertical movement (positive up, negative down).

Enlargements

You describe an enlargement by naming the **centre** and the **scale factor**.

When a shape is enlarged, the image is mathematically similar to the object.

- If the scale factor is greater than 1 then the object gets bigger
- If the scale factor is between 0 and 1 then the object gets smaller
- If the scale factor is 1 then the object remains the same

If *X* is the centre of the enlargement and *k* is the scale factor then *A* gets mapped to *A'* where *A'* lies on the line *XA* (extended if necessary) and *XA'* = *k* × *XA*.

Example

Enlarge the triangle *ABC* with vertices *A* (2, 4), *B* (4, 0) and *C* (2, 2) by scale factor 3 with centre of enlargement *X* (1, 2).

To find *A'* draw the line *XA* extended through *A*.

Mark the point *A'* on this line such that $XA' = 3 \times XA$.

So *A'* is the point (4, 8).

Repeat for *B'* and *C'*.

The triangle *A'B'C'* is an enlargement of triangle *ABC*.

You use the same principle when *k* is a fraction.

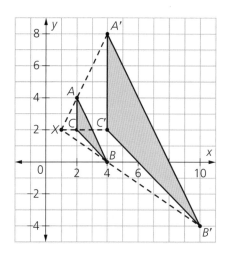

Example

Enlarge the quadrilateral *ABCD* with vertices *A* (−1, 1), *B* (1, 3), *C* (3, 3) and *D* (3, −1) by scale factor $\frac{1}{2}$ with centre of enlargement *X* (−3, −3).

To find *A'* draw the line *XA*. Mark the point *A'* on this line such that $XA' = \frac{1}{2} \times XA$.

Repeat for *B'*, *C'* and *D'*.

Join *A'B'C'D'*.

The quadrilateral *A'B'C'D'* with *A'*(−2, −1), *B'*(−1, 0), *C'*(0, 0) and *D'*(0, −2) is an enlargement of quadrilateral *ABCD*.

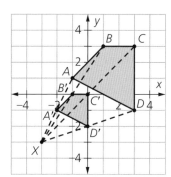

Negative scale factor

When the scale factor of enlargement is negative the image is on the other side of the centre of enlargement from the object.

Example

Enlarge the quadrilateral *ABCD* with vertices *A* (2, 1), *B* (4, 2), *C* (4, 1) and *D* (3, −1) by scale factor −2 with centre of enlargement *X* (1, 0).

To find *A'* draw the line *AX* and extend past *X*.

Mark the point *A'* on this line such that $XA' = 2 \times XA$.

Repeat for *B'*, *C'* and *D'*.

The quadrilateral *A'B'C'D'* with *A'*(−1, −2), *B'*(−5, −4), *C'*(−5, −2), *D'*(−3, 2) is an enlargement of quadrilateral *ABCD*.

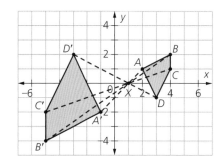

Using matrices

You can use a matrix to describe a transformation.

If a transformation can be represented by a matrix, then the transformation must map the origin to itself.

So:
- the centre of a rotation or enlargement that can be represented by a matrix must be the origin
- the mirror line of a reflection that can be represented by a matrix must pass through the origin.

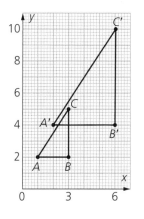

Example

Find the image of the triangle *ABC* with *A* (1, 2), *B* (3, 2) and *C* (3, 5) under the transformation represented by the matrix M $\begin{pmatrix} 2 & 0 \\ 0 & 2 \end{pmatrix}$. What transformation does M represent?

Put the position vectors in a 2 × 3 matrix:

$$\begin{pmatrix} 1 & 3 & 3 \\ 2 & 2 & 5 \end{pmatrix}$$

Then multiply this matrix by **M**.

$$\begin{pmatrix} 2 & 0 \\ 0 & 2 \end{pmatrix} \begin{pmatrix} 1 & 3 & 3 \\ 2 & 2 & 5 \end{pmatrix} = \begin{pmatrix} 2 & 6 & 6 \\ 4 & 4 & 10 \end{pmatrix}$$
$$2 \times 2 \quad\quad 2 \times 3 \quad\quad A' \ B' \ \ C'$$

The image of triangle *ABC* is triangle *A'B'C'* where *A'* is (2, 4), *B'* is (6, 4) and *C'* is (6, 10).

M represents an enlargement, scale factor 2, centre (0, 0).

Example

Find the image of triangle *ABC*, with *A* (1, 1), *B* (3, 1) and *C* (3, 2) under the

transformation represented by the matrix M $\begin{pmatrix} 0 & -1 \\ 1 & 0 \end{pmatrix}$. What transformation does M

represent?

Put the position vectors in a 2 × 3 matrix:

$$\begin{pmatrix} 1 & 3 & 3 \\ 1 & 1 & 2 \end{pmatrix}$$

Then multiply this matrix by **M**:

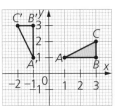

$$\begin{matrix} A & B & C & & A' & B' & C' \\ \begin{pmatrix} 0 & -1 \\ 1 & 0 \end{pmatrix} & \begin{pmatrix} 1 & 3 & 3 \\ 1 & 1 & 2 \end{pmatrix} & = & \begin{pmatrix} -1 & -1 & -2 \\ 1 & 3 & 3 \end{pmatrix} \end{matrix}$$

A', *B'* and *C'* are the images of *A*, *B* and *C*.

M represents a rotation of 90° anticlockwise, centre (0, 0).

Finding the matrix of a transformation

You can find the matrix that represents a transformation by looking at the unit square and its image.

For example, for a rotation of 90° anticlockwise, centre (0, 0).

$$\overrightarrow{OA} = \begin{pmatrix} 1 \\ 0 \end{pmatrix}, \ \overrightarrow{OA'} = \begin{pmatrix} 0 \\ 1 \end{pmatrix}$$

$$\overrightarrow{OB} = \begin{pmatrix} 0 \\ 1 \end{pmatrix}, \ \overrightarrow{OB'} = \begin{pmatrix} -1 \\ 0 \end{pmatrix}$$

Combine these two position vectors $\overrightarrow{OA'}$ and $\overrightarrow{OB'}$ in a 2 × 2

matrix: $\begin{pmatrix} 0 & -1 \\ 1 & 0 \end{pmatrix}$

The matrix $\begin{pmatrix} 0 & -1 \\ 1 & 0 \end{pmatrix}$ represents a rotation of 90° anticlockwise, as was seen in the example above.

Example

Find the matrix that represents a reflection in the *x*-axis.

Draw the unit square and its image.

$$\overrightarrow{OA} = \begin{pmatrix} 1 \\ 0 \end{pmatrix}, \ \overrightarrow{OA'} = \begin{pmatrix} 1 \\ 0 \end{pmatrix}$$

$$\overrightarrow{OB} = \begin{pmatrix} 0 \\ 1 \end{pmatrix}, \ \overrightarrow{OB'} = \begin{pmatrix} 0 \\ -1 \end{pmatrix}$$

Combine these two position vectors $\overrightarrow{OA'}$ and $\overrightarrow{OB'}$ in a

2 × 2 matrix: $\begin{pmatrix} 1 & 0 \\ 0 & -1 \end{pmatrix}$

The matrix $\begin{pmatrix} 1 & 0 \\ 0 & -1 \end{pmatrix}$ represents a reflection in the *x*-axis.

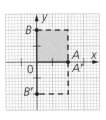

Example

Find the matrix which represents a reflection in the line *y* = *x*.

$$\overrightarrow{OA} = \begin{pmatrix} 1 \\ 0 \end{pmatrix} \ \overrightarrow{OA'} = \begin{pmatrix} 0 \\ 1 \end{pmatrix}$$

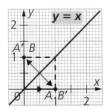

$\overrightarrow{OB} = \begin{pmatrix} 0 \\ 1 \end{pmatrix}$ $\overrightarrow{OB'} = \begin{pmatrix} 1 \\ 0 \end{pmatrix}$

The matrix $\begin{pmatrix} 0 & 1 \\ 1 & 0 \end{pmatrix}$ represents a reflection in $y = x$.

Finding the transformation that a matrix represents

Example
Describe the transformation with matrix $\begin{pmatrix} 2 & 0 \\ 0 & 2 \end{pmatrix}$.

The first column tells you that $\overrightarrow{OA'} = \begin{pmatrix} 2 \\ 0 \end{pmatrix}$.

The second column tells you that $\overrightarrow{OB'} = \begin{pmatrix} 0 \\ 2 \end{pmatrix}$.

$\begin{pmatrix} 2 & 0 \\ 0 & 2 \end{pmatrix}$ represents an enlargement, scale factor 2, centre (0, 0).

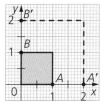

Example
What transformation is represented by the matrix $\begin{pmatrix} 0 & 1 \\ -1 & 0 \end{pmatrix}$?

The first column tells you that the image of $\overrightarrow{OA}$ is $\begin{pmatrix} 0 \\ -1 \end{pmatrix}$.

The second column tells you that the image of $\overrightarrow{OB}$ is $\begin{pmatrix} 1 \\ 0 \end{pmatrix}$.

$\begin{pmatrix} 0 & 1 \\ -1 & 0 \end{pmatrix}$ represents a rotation of 90° clockwise, centre (0, 0).

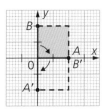

Inverse matrix
If the matrix **M** maps A to B then $\mathbf{M}^{-1}$, which is called the inverse of **M**, maps B to A.
So $\mathbf{M}^{-1}$ undoes the effect of **M**.
You can "undo" a clockwise rotation by an anticlockwise rotation.
You can "undo" a reflection by another identical reflection.

You can "undo" an enlargement of scale factor k by an enlargement of scale factor $\frac{1}{k}$.

Notation
The following letters are used:
M to represent a reflection (M for mirror)   R to represent a rotation
T to represent a translation   E to represent an enlargement

M(A) is the image of A under the rotation M.
RM(A) is the image of A under (i) the reflection M followed by (ii) the rotation R.

> So RM(A) represents M followed by R. This is easy to
> remember because M is next to A and so acts on A first.

Exam question   CIE 0580 June '07 Paper 4 Q2 b and f

(a) Draw triangle *ABC* with A (2, 1), B (3, 3) and C (5, 1).

(b) A transformation is represented by the matrix $\begin{pmatrix} 1 & 0 \\ -1 & 1 \end{pmatrix}$.

   (i) Draw the image of triangle *ABC* under this transformation. Label
      this $A_3B_3C_3$

   (ii) Find the matrix which represents the transformation
      that maps triangle $A_3B_3C_3$ onto triangle *ABC*.

(a) and (b) (i) $\begin{pmatrix} 1 & 0 \\ -1 & 1 \end{pmatrix}\begin{pmatrix} 2 & 3 & 5 \\ 1 & 3 & 1 \end{pmatrix} = \begin{pmatrix} 2 & 3 & 5 \\ -1 & 0 & -4 \end{pmatrix}$

    A_3 is (2, −1), B_3 is (3, 0) and C_3 is (5, −4).

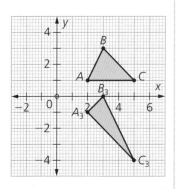

(Continued)

Exam question (Continued)

(ii) The determinant of $\begin{pmatrix} 1 & 0 \\ -1 & 1 \end{pmatrix} = (1 \times 1) - (0 \times -1) = 1$

so the inverse of $\begin{pmatrix} 1 & 0 \\ -1 & 1 \end{pmatrix} = \begin{pmatrix} 1 & 0 \\ 1 & 1 \end{pmatrix}$

The matrix which represents the transformation that

maps triangle $A_3B_3C_3$ onto triangle $ABC = \begin{pmatrix} 1 & 0 \\ 1 & 1 \end{pmatrix}$.

Exam question

CIE 0580 June '06 Paper 4 Q7

Transformation T is a translation by the vector $\begin{pmatrix} 3 \\ 2 \end{pmatrix}$.

Transformation M is a reflection in the line $y = x$.

    (a) **The point A has coordinates (2, 1).**

        Find the coordinates of

        (i)   **T(A).**

        (ii) **MT(A).**

    (b) **Find the 2 by 2 matrix M, which represents the transformation M.**

    (c) **Show that, for any value of k, the point $Q\,(k-2, k-3)$ maps onto a point on the line $y = x$ following the transformation TM(Q).**

    (d) **Find M^{-1}, the inverse of the matrix M.**

    (e) **N is the matrix such that $N + \begin{pmatrix} 0 & 3 \\ 1 & 0 \end{pmatrix} = \begin{pmatrix} 0 & 4 \\ 0 & 0 \end{pmatrix}$.**

        (i)   **Write down the matrix N.**

        (ii) **Describe completely the single transformation represented by N.**

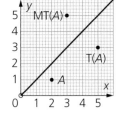

(a)   (i)   T is the translation by the vector $\begin{pmatrix} 3 \\ 2 \end{pmatrix}$ so it moves

        points 3 to the right and 2 up.

        So T(A) is (5, 3).

    (ii) MT(A) = M(5,3) = (3,5)

(b) M maps $\begin{pmatrix} 1 \\ 0 \end{pmatrix}$ to $\begin{pmatrix} 0 \\ 1 \end{pmatrix}$ so the first column of **M** is $\begin{pmatrix} 0 \\ 1 \end{pmatrix}$.

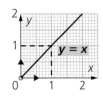

    M maps $\begin{pmatrix} 0 \\ 1 \end{pmatrix}$ to $\begin{pmatrix} 1 \\ 0 \end{pmatrix}$ so the second column of **M** is $\begin{pmatrix} 1 \\ 0 \end{pmatrix}$.

    So **M** $= \begin{pmatrix} 0 & 1 \\ 1 & 0 \end{pmatrix}$

(c) M(Q) $= \begin{pmatrix} 0 & 1 \\ 1 & 0 \end{pmatrix}\begin{pmatrix} k-2 \\ k-3 \end{pmatrix} = \begin{pmatrix} k-3 \\ k-2 \end{pmatrix}$

    TM(Q) $= T\begin{pmatrix} k-3 \\ k-2 \end{pmatrix} = \begin{pmatrix} k-3 \\ k-2 \end{pmatrix} + \begin{pmatrix} 3 \\ 2 \end{pmatrix} = \begin{pmatrix} k \\ k \end{pmatrix}$

    So TM(Q) is a point on the line $y = x$.

(d) If **M** represents a reflection in a line then $\mathbf{M}^{-1}$ represents a reflection in the same

    line. So $\mathbf{M}^{-1}$ is the same as **M**. So $\mathbf{M}^{-1} = \begin{pmatrix} 0 & 1 \\ 1 & 0 \end{pmatrix}$.

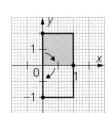

(e)   (i)   If **N** $+ \begin{pmatrix} 0 & 3 \\ 1 & 0 \end{pmatrix} = \begin{pmatrix} 0 & 4 \\ 0 & 0 \end{pmatrix}$ then **N** $= \begin{pmatrix} 0 & 4 \\ 0 & 0 \end{pmatrix} - \begin{pmatrix} 0 & 3 \\ 1 & 0 \end{pmatrix} = \begin{pmatrix} 0 & 1 \\ -1 & 0 \end{pmatrix}$.

    (ii) Under the transformation N the image of

        (1, 0) is (0, −1) and the image of (0, 1) is (1, 0).

        N represents a rotation of 90° clockwise, centre (0, 0).

Questions

1.

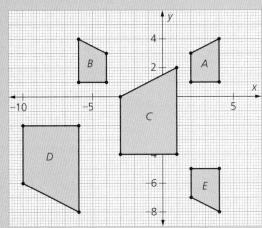

Describe the transformation which maps:

(a) *A* onto *B*

(b) *A* onto *C*

(c) *B* onto *D*

(d) *A* onto *E*

2. (a) Draw a pair of axes with *x* and *y* from −8 to 8 and 1 cm per unit on both.
  Draw and label the triangle T_1 which has vertices (2, 2), (5, 2) and (5, 4)

(b) (i) Draw and label the triangle T_2 which is the image of T_1 under a rotation of 90° anticlockwise, centre (7, 2).

  (ii) Draw and label the triangle T_3 which is the image of T_2 under a reflection in the line $y = −4$.

(c) (i) Draw and label the triangle T_4 which is the image of T_1 under a rotation of 90° clockwise, centre (−4, 2).

  (ii) Draw and label the triangle T_5 which is the image of T_4 under a reflection in the *y*-axis.

  (iii) Draw and label the triangle T_6 which is the image of T_1 under a rotation of 90° anticlockwise, centre (−2, 0).

(d) Show that the vector $\begin{pmatrix} -3 \\ 1 \end{pmatrix}$ translates T_3 onto T_5.

(e) Find the vector which translates T_2 onto T_6.

Extended

3. (a) Draw a pair of axes with *x* and *y* from −8 to 8 and 1 cm per unit on both.
  Draw and label the parallelogram P_1 which has vertices (2, 2), (5, 2), (3, 4) and (6, 4).

(b) (i) Draw and label the parallelogram P_2 which is the image of P_1 under a rotation of 180°, centre the origin.

  (ii) Draw and label the parallelogram P_3 which is the image of P_2 under a reflection in the line $x = 1$.

(c) Draw and label the parallelogram P_4 which is the image of P_1 under reflection in the *y*-axis.

(d) Find the vector which translates P_3 onto P_4.

(e) To what point is (2, 2) mapped under the transformation described in (b) (i) followed by the transformation described in (b) (ii) followed by the transformation described in (d)?

(f) To what point is (2, 2) mapped under the transformation described in (c)?

4. (a) Draw a pair of axes with *x* and *y* from −8 to 8 with 1 cm per unit on both.
  Draw and label the triangle with vertices *A*(1, 1), *B*(2, 5) and *C* (4, 3).

(b) Draw the rotation of triangle *ABC* by 90° anticlockwise centre (−1, 2). Label the image triangle $A_1B_1C_1$.

(c) Draw the reflection of triangle *ABC* in the line $y = −x$. Label the image triangle $A_2B_2C_2$.

5. Find the transformations represented by the following matrices:

(a) $\begin{pmatrix} 1 & 0 \\ 0 & -1 \end{pmatrix}$ (b) $\begin{pmatrix} 0 & -1 \\ 1 & 0 \end{pmatrix}$ (c) $\begin{pmatrix} 0 & -1 \\ -1 & 0 \end{pmatrix}$

6. Find the matrices representing these transformations:

(a) rotation of 180° about the origin

(b) enlargement scale factor 2, centre the origin.

Answers

1 Numbers
1. $\sqrt{7}$
2. a) 84 b) 83 or 89 c) 85
3. a) 7 b) 2
4. a) 1, 3, 7 and 21 b) 1, 2, 4, 7, 14 and 28 c) 7
5. a) $\sqrt{49}$ b) $\sqrt{121}$
   c) $\sqrt{64}$ or $\sqrt{16}$ d) $\sqrt{15}$
6. a) $2 \times 3 \times 5$ b) $2^3 \times 3$
   c) 2×3^2 d) $2^2 \times 7$
   e) $3 \times 5 \times 7$ f) 2^6
7. a) 6 b) 4 c) 3
8. a) 960 b) 840 c) 252

2 Sequences
1. a) $34750 + 250n$ b) 12
2. a) $0.8 + 0.2n$ b) £2.40
   c) 21 d) 99p
3. a) 4, 9, 14,... b) 0, 3, 8,...
   c) 1, 3, 6 d) $\frac{2}{3}, \frac{9}{6}, \frac{28}{9}$
4. a) 160, 320 b) 216, 343
   c) 72, 98 d) $\frac{13}{49}, \frac{15}{64}$
5. a)

Diagram	1	2	3	4	5
Sticks	5	9	13	17	21

   b) 101 c) $4n + 1$ d) 32
6. a) 972 b) 49 c) 26 d) $48x^6$
7. 120

3 Sets
1. a) $A \cap B \cap C$
   b) A
   c) $A \cap B$
   d) $A \cup B$
2. a)

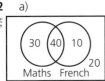

   b) 40
3. a)

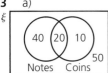

   b) 20

4. a)

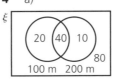

   b) 30

4 Calculations
1. 3.68 cm
2. a) 64 b) 1331 c) 50.4
   d) 4.12 e) -4.64 f) 19
3. 7 cm
4. 6 cm
5. a) 0.6^3 0.6^2 0.6 $\sqrt{0.6}$ $\sqrt[3]{0.6}$
   b) $\sqrt[3]{6}$ $\sqrt{6}$ 6 6^2 6^3
6. a) $4 + 15 \div (5 - 2) \times 5 = 29$
   b) $3 + (2^2 \times 3) = 15$
   c) $5 + 3 \times (2 + 7) = 32$
7. a) 6.10 b) 0.246 c) 6.24

5 Directed numbers
1. The average temperature in Montreal is shown below:

Month	Jan	Feb	Mar	Apr	May	Jun
Avg Temp	-11	-9	-3	5	13	18

Jul	Aug	Sep	Oct	Nov	Dec
21	19	15	8	1	-7

   a) 32° b) $-12°$
2. a) 14 b) 8 c) -6 d) 19
   e) 6 f) -4
3. $-£395.20$
4. 5 cm above flood level

6 Fractions and decimals
1. 120
2. 20
3. a) $\frac{3}{8}$ b) 0.12
4. a) $18\frac{2}{3}$ b) $14\frac{3}{20}$
   c) $5\frac{11}{24}$ d) $1\frac{62}{85}$
5. 0.8 81% $\frac{41}{50}$ $\frac{21}{25}$ 0.85
6. a) $x < y$ b) $y - x > x - y$
   c) $12x < y^2$
7. a) the smallest is $\frac{3}{100}$
   b) the largest is 37%
   c) the two that are equal are 0.037 and 3.7%
8. a) $\frac{2}{9}$ b) $\frac{61}{99}$

7 Standard form
1. 3.46×10^3 km
2. 1.226×10^4 km
3. 6.3781×10^6 m
4. 299 800 000 m/s
5. a) 0.000 0640 b) 0.000 000 0143
   c) 0.000 001 71 d) 0.000 005 49
6. a) 1.07×10^9 b) 3.49×10^9
   c) 1.56×10^{-2} d) 3.70×10^{-2}
   e) 7.07×10^{-2} f) 8.26×10^{-3}
   g) 1.22×10^9 h) 8.37×10^{-2}
   i) 5.63×10^{-2}
7. a) 1.43×10^{13} b) 6.09×10^{22}
   c) 9.36×10^3 d) 1.66×10^2
   e) 3.99×10^{12} f) 9.76×10^{-15}
8. a) 5.4×10^9 (to 2 sf) b) 5.8%
   c) 1.3×10^{10} (to 2 sf)
9. a) 3×10^4 kg b) 5×10^8 m³
   c) 1×10^6 cm³ d) 1×10^6 g
   e) 1g cm³ f) 180g
10. 7.91×10^{-3} people per m²
11. 4.1×10^4 km
12. $\$2.58 \times 10^{12}$

8 Estimation and limits of accuracy
1. a) i) 4 ii) 10 iii) 10 iv) 7
   b) i) 3.84 ii) 10.0
   iii) 10.5 iv) 7.31
2. a) 300 cm² b) 312 cm²
3. a) 20,000 b) 20900 to (3sf)
4. 17 050 ft
5. a) 73.425 and 73.435
   b) 7315 and 7325
   c) 7319.5 and 7320.5
   d) 147.0365 and 147.0375
   e) 99.95 and 100.5
   f) 95 and 150
6. a) 670km b) 680km c) 650km
7. The lower bound is 2,935,000 and the upper bound is 2,945,000
8. 9.6 ms⁻¹ and 9.8 ms⁻¹
9. a) 6945 m² and 6955 m²
   b) 94.5m and 95.5m
   c) 72.7m and 73.6m
10. 490 and 508
11. 11.2cm and 11.4cm
12. $17 \leqslant s < 29$

9 Ratio, proportion and rate
1. $112.90
2. a) $120 $200 $240
   b) 2 : 5
3. a) £354 b) €381
4. $350
5. a) 5022 Chinese Yuan
   b) 119.47 euros

6 a) $s = 3t^2$ b) $s = 147$ c) $t = 11$
   d) s increases by a factor of 4
7 a) $m = 8l^3$ b) 2.744 kg
   c) 10.5 cm
   d) l has increased by 10%
8 a) $l = \dfrac{8820}{d^2}$ b) $l = 2205$
   c) $d = 14$ d) d doubles

10 Percentages

1 a) £2205   b) 10.25%
2 $804.96
3 a) £1210   b) 10%
   c) 10.5%
4 €763.75
5 15%
6 20
7 €2.40 interest
8 £60
9 James, $85.1 \div 1.15 = 74$
10 £18
11 18 cm by 25 cm
12 27 000
13 1.4 m
14 1200
15 $1250
16 €500
17 a) –   b) $1 125 000
18 $16 400

11 Time and speed

1 71.8 km h^{-1}
2 680 km h^{-1}
3 a) 8 h 50 min
   b) 8 h 30 min
   c) 20 minutes
   d) 771 km h^{-1} and 802 km h^{-1}
4 a) 8 hours   b) 2300
   c) €1093.50
5 21.6 litres

12 Graphs in practical situations

1 a) $50   b) $130
   c) 4 hours   d) 2 hours
2 a) This happened after it had
      travelled 200 km.
   b) It rested for 30 minutes.
   c) It travelled a further 90 km
   d) It spend 3 hours at the game.
   e) It took 3 hours to get home
   f) Average speed is $290 \div 3 =$
      9.67 km h^{-1} (to 3sf)
3 a) 5 minutes   b) Speed was
      increasing   c) 66 km/h
   d) 16 minutes   e) 76.4 km/h

4 a) 1 minute   b) 6 km
   c) Gradually decreasing   d) 7.5 km
   e) An under-estimate

13 Graphs of functions

1 a)

x	0	1	2	3	4	5	6
y	1	−4	−7	−8	−7	−4	1

   b) & c)

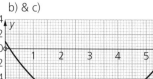

   d) $y = 0$: $x = 0.2$ or $x = 5.8$
      $y = -5$: $x = 1.3$ or $x = 4.7$

2 a)

x	−5	−4	−3	−2	−1	0	1
y	15	4	−5	−12	−17	−20	−21

2	3	4	5	6	7
−20	−17	−12	−5	4	15

   b)

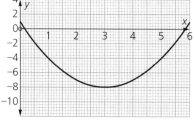

   c)

x	−5	−4	−3	−2	−1	0
y	−4.8	−6.0	−8	−12	−24.0	n/a

1	2	3	4	5	6	7
24.0	12.0	8.0	6	4.8	4	3.4

   d)

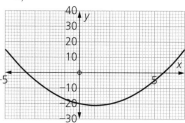

   e) −2 and 6
3 a)

x	−3	−2	−1	0	1	2	3	4	5
y	11	4	−1	−4	−5	−4	−1	4	11

   b) & c)

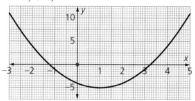

   d) $x = -1.2$ or $x = 3.2$
   e) $x = -2.2$ or $x = 4.2$
   f) −5 at $x = 1$
4 a) i) −6   ii) 14
   b) i) −3.2, −0.3 and 2
      ii) −3, −0.7 and 2.2
   c) $-6 < k < 21$
   d) $x > 1$ and $x < -2$

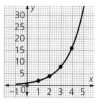

5 $x = 3.3$

14 Straight line graphs

1 2.5
2 $y = 6x - 23$
3 a) (2, 5)   b) 7.21   c) $\dfrac{2}{3}$
   d) $3y - 2x = 11$
4 (4, 0) and (0, 6)
5

x	0	5	10
y	−2	1	4

6 $y = 0.5x$

15 Algebraic formulae

1 a) 0.5 ms^{-2} b) 0.04 ms^{-2}
   c) 3 ms^{-2}
2 32 m
3 a) 33.5 m^3 b) $\sqrt[3]{\dfrac{3V}{4\pi}}$ c) 3.63 mm
4 7 500 000 000
5 3.5
6 344
7 a) $x = \dfrac{p - n}{m}$ b) $x = \dfrac{c - ab}{a}$
   c) $x = qr - p$ d) $x = \dfrac{rt - pq}{p}$
   e) $x = \dfrac{h}{u}$ f) $x = \dfrac{k - wb}{w}$
   g) $x = \dfrac{d - bc}{ac}$ h) $x = \dfrac{a}{c - b}$
8 a) $w = \dfrac{cd - b}{a}$ b) $y = cx + ct - b$
   c) $z = \dfrac{ab}{c}$ d) $h = \dfrac{a}{b}$
   e) $o = \dfrac{h}{2}$ f) $r = t^2$
   g) $t = ad + cd - b$ h) $g = \dfrac{aq}{p}$

9 a) $x = \dfrac{r}{m - n}$ b) $x = \dfrac{d - b}{a - c}$

c) $x = \dfrac{d}{a - b}$ d) $x = \dfrac{pn - m}{p + q}$

e) $x = \dfrac{A - B}{C}$ f) $x = \dfrac{bc}{a - c}$

10 a) $A = \dfrac{s}{t - 1}$ b) $R = \dfrac{b}{a - b}$

c) $e = \dfrac{d - b}{a - c}$ d) $p = \dfrac{cd}{a - bd}$

e) $Q = \dfrac{cd}{b - c}$ f) $x = \dfrac{(cd)^2 + b}{a}$

g) $y = \dfrac{pq^2 - n}{m}$ h) $q = \dfrac{n - cm}{a + bc}$

i) $t = \dfrac{a}{b + c^2}$ j) $k = \dfrac{b\sqrt{p}}{a - \sqrt{p}}$

16 Expanding and factorising

1 a) $7p + 21q$ b) $30m - 42n$

c) $3a + 24b$

2 a) $6x^2 + 7x + 2$

b) $15x^2 + 26x + 8$

c) $12t^2 - 20t + 3$

d) $6y^2 - 29y + 9$

e) $14z^2 + 19z - 3$

f) $27r^2 + 12r - 4$

g) $14e^2 - 15e - 11$

h) $40q^2 - 19q - 3$

i) $9p^2 - 1$ j) $49y^2 - 4$

k) $2k^2 + 7k + 3$

l) $10v^2 - 3v - 1$

3 a) $x^2 + 5x + 6$ b) $x^2 + 9x + 20$

c) $t^2 + 3t + 2$ d) $6q^2 - q - 1$

e) $10y^2 - 11y - 6$ f) $25m^2 - 1$

g) $4y^2 - 1$ h) $9p^2 + 12p + 4$

i) $4q^2 - 4q + 1$

j) $10d^2 - 11de - 6e^2$

k) $20p^2 + 17pq + 3q^2$

l) $14s^2 - 13st + 3t^2$

4 a) $x^2 + 6x + 9$ b) $y^2 + 10y + 25$

c) $y^2 - 8y + 16$ d) $x^2 - 12z + 36$

e) $4w^2 - 12w + 9$

f) $25t^2 - 20t + 4$

g) $6a^2 + 5ab + b^2$

h) $15m^2 - 13mn + 2n^2$

i) $15p^2 - 14pq - 8q^2$

j) $10x^2 - 19xy + 6y^2$

k) $9c^2 + 12cd + 4d^2$

l) $25p^2 - 30pq + 9q^2$

5 a) $(x + 3)(x + 6)$ b) $(x - 5)(x + 4)$

c) $(x - 5)(x - 2)$ d) $(x + 8)(x - 5)$

e) $(x - 7)(x + 6)$ f) $(x + 3)(x + 4)$

g) $(x + 6)(x - 4)$ h) $(x + 4)(x - 4)$

i) $x(x + 3)$ j) $(x + 5)(x - 5)$

6 a) $(x - 6)(x + 1)$ b) $(x + 2)(x + 3)$

c) $(x + 6)(x - 1)$ d) $(x - 2)(x - 3)$

e) $(x - 10)(x + 6)$

f) $(x + 9)(x - 4)$

g) $(x - 11)(x - 9)$

h) $(x + 1)(x - 1)$

i) $(x + 12)(x - 11)$ j) $(x + 3)^2$

k) $(x - 5)^2$ l) $(x + 10)(x - 10)$

7 a) $(x + 3)(x + 4)$ b) $(x + 5)(x + 2)$

c) $(x - 6)(x + 1)$ d) $(x - 2)(x - 3)$

e) $(2x - 3)(x + 4)$

f) $(3x + 2)(x + 3)$

g) $(2x + 1)(2x + 5)$

h) $(5x + 8)(x + 1)$

8 a) $a(a + 5b)$ b) $r(r + 2)$

c) $(t + 6)(t - 6)$ d) $(b + 3)(b + 8)$

e) $(2p + 9)(2p + 1)$

f) $(5q + 2)(q - 2)$

9 a) $(x + 1)(x + 2)$

b) $(y - 3)(y + 3)$ c) $z(z + 2)$

d) $(n - 3)(n + 2)$

e) $(2p - 5)(2p + 1)$

f) $(3q - 2)(q - 2)$

10 a) $(x - 4)(x - 5)$

b) $(x + 2)(x - 5)$

c) $(4x - 3)(x - 2)$

d) $(3x + 1)(2x - 5)$

e) $(8x - 5)(x - 1)$

f) $(3x + 1)(2x + 5)$

17 Algebraic fractions

1 a) $\dfrac{13x + 8}{15}$ b) $\dfrac{8x - 9}{6}$

c) $\dfrac{12x + 5}{12}$ d) $\dfrac{23x + 11}{14}$

e) $\dfrac{9x + 14}{12}$ f) $\dfrac{15x + 16}{30}$

g) $\dfrac{-3x - 5}{12}$ h) $\dfrac{22x + 15}{20}$

2 a) $\dfrac{13x + 1}{10}$ b) $\dfrac{23x + 2}{20}$

c) $\dfrac{4x - 5}{3}$ d) $\dfrac{3x}{2}$

e) $\dfrac{14x + 3}{6}$ f) $\dfrac{27x + 14}{12}$

3 a) $\dfrac{5x + 7}{(x + 2)(x + 1)}$

b) $\dfrac{7x + 17}{(x + 2)(x + 3)}$

c) $\dfrac{12x + 2}{(x - 1)(x + 1)}$

d) $\dfrac{3x + 4}{(x + 3)(x + 2)}$

e) $\dfrac{17x + 9}{(2x + 3)(3x - 1)}$

f) $\dfrac{32x - 11}{(3x + 1)(4x - 3)}$

4 a) $x + 1$ b) $x + 2$

c) $2x + 1$ d) $x - 3$

e) $x - 5$ f) $2x - 1$

g) $x + 1$ h) $5x - 1$

18 Functions

1 a) 7   b) 4   c) 0

2 $\dfrac{2x + 1}{x - 1}$

3 a) 9   b) $(x + 1)^2$ c) 3 or -5

d) -3

4 a) -1 b) 6   c) $(y - 2)^2$

19 Indices

1 a) a^5 b) b^{17} c) c^{11} d) x^{13}

e) y^7 f) z^7 g) q^{12} h) w^{12}

i) r^2 j) s^{21} k) t^4 l) w^{16}

2 a) $a = 4$ b) $a = 1$ c) $a = 0$

d) $a = 20$ e) $a = 16$ f) $a = 7$

g) $a = 4$ h) $a = 3$ i) $a = 6$

3 a) $3x^4$ b) $2y^2$ c) $12z$ d) $4a^2$

e) $8c^4$ f) $12h^2$

4 a) $8ab^7$ b) $15m^3n^4$ c) $4r^5t^2$

d) g^2h^{10}

5 a) $8x^6y^3$ b) $9x^6y^8$

c) $64x^4y^6$

d) $125x^6y^{15}$

e) $81x^{12}y^{14}$ f) $64x^{14}y^6$

g) $432x^{14}y^{21}$ h) $200x^{15}y^{23}$

6 a) 64   b) 81   c) 125

d) 121   e) $\dfrac{1}{8}$ f) $\dfrac{1}{100}$

g) 1   h) 169   i) $\dfrac{1}{64}$ j) $\dfrac{1}{8}$

k) $\dfrac{4}{9}$ l) $\dfrac{625}{81}$ m) 4   n) $\dfrac{125}{8}$

o) $\dfrac{81}{16}$

7 a) $\dfrac{1}{5}$ b) $\dfrac{1}{4}$ c) $\dfrac{1}{3}$ d) $\dfrac{1}{2}$ e) $\dfrac{1}{2}$

f) $\dfrac{1}{3}$ g) $\dfrac{1}{5}$ h) $\dfrac{1}{2}$ i) -1 j) $-\dfrac{1}{4}$

k) $-\dfrac{1}{3}$ l) $-\dfrac{1}{9}$

8 a) $\dfrac{1}{81}$ b) $\dfrac{1}{125}$ c) $\dfrac{1}{49}$

d) 2   e) 8   f) 125   g) $\dfrac{9}{16}$

h) $\dfrac{3}{4}$ i) $\dfrac{2}{5}$

20 Solving linear equations

1 a) $3a = 135$ b) $a = 45$

2 a) $n + 1, n + 2$

b) $n + n + 1 + n + 2 = 144$

c) $n = 47$; 47, 48, 49

3 a) $x = 5$ b) $x = 2$ c) $x = 1$

d) $x = 4$ e) $x = -2$ f) $x = 6$

4 a) 3   b) 3   c) 4   d) 3   e) 1

f) 1

5 a) $x = 5, y = 1$ b) $u = 4, v = -1$
c) $p = 7, q = -2$
d) $a = 5, b = -2$
e) $p = 3, q = 2$
f) $b = 2, c = -3$

6 a) $m = 3, n = 4$
b) $p = 5, q = -1$
c) $u = 1, v = 3$
d) $p = 5, q = 3$
e) $r = 3, s = -2$
f) $x = 21, y = 12$

7 a) $5x + 2y = 246$
   $2x + 3y = 149$
b) $x = €40, y = €23$

8 a) $p + q = 95$
   $p - q = 21$
b) $p = 58, q = 37$

9 a) $3s + 5a = 62$
   $7s + 3a = 71$
b) $s = \$6.50$
   $a = \$8.50$

10 a) $x = 4, y = 9$ b) $x = -2, y = 3$
c) $x = 2, y = 5$ d) $x = -3, y = -5$
e) $x = 5, y = -4$ f) $x = 6, y = 3$

21 Solving quadratic equations

1 a) $x = -3, x = -4$
b) $y = -2, y = -11$
c) $m = -1, m = 6$
d) $a = 2, a = 3$
e) $z = -2, z = 6$
f) $z = -1$ g) $c = -3, c = -12$
h) $t = 9$ i) $r = 0, r = 6$
j) $t = 0, t = -11$
k) $w = 0, w = 3$ l) $k = 0, k = -1$

2 a) $x = -1 \pm \sqrt{2}$
b) $x = 2 \pm \sqrt{7}$ c) $x = -6$
d) $x = -10 \pm \sqrt{95}$
e) $x = 1, x = -9$ f) $x = 1 \pm \sqrt{8}$

3 a) $x = -3, x = 1$
b) $x = -3, x = 1$
c) $x = \dfrac{-5 \pm \sqrt{23}}{2}$
d) $x = -2 \pm \sqrt{10}$

4 a) -4 b) $(x + 2)^2 \geqslant 0$
c) $x + 2 = 0$ when $x = -2$

5 a) i) $n + 5$
   ii) Snakes Alive $\dfrac{500}{n}$;
   Edible Reptiles $\dfrac{570}{n + 5}$
b) 25

6 a) $x + 23$
b) $x^2 + (x + 23)^2 = 65^2$
c) 33

22 Solving inequalities

1

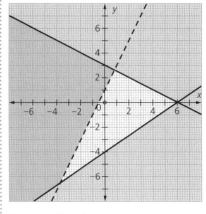

2 $y < 12 - 3x$
$y > x - 2$
$y \leqslant x + 6$
$y \geqslant 12 - 12x$

3

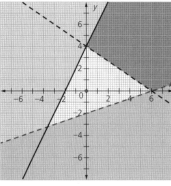

4

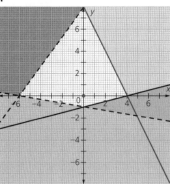

5

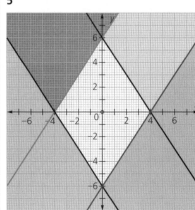

23 Linear programming

1 a)

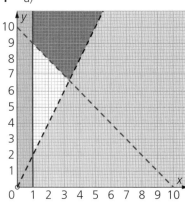

b) 19 c) 7

2 a) $x \geqslant 5$ $y < 11$ $y \geqslant x$
b) & c)

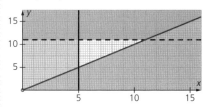

d) $5x + 4y$
e) i) $\$45$ ii) $\$99$

3 a) $3x + y \leqslant 20$
   $y < 2x$ $x + y \geqslant 8$
b)

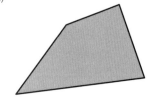

c) $\$35$

24 Angles and polygons

1 a) Rectangle b) Square
c) Parallelogram
d) Rhombus
e) Pentagon
f) Hexagon
g) Trapezium
h) Octagon
i) Kite

2 a) $x = 87.5°$ b) $x = 30°$

3 a)

b)

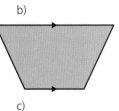

c)

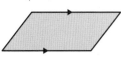

d)

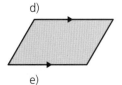

e)

f)

4 a) Quadrilateral b) Trapezium
   c) Parallelogram d) Rhombus
   e) Rectangle f) Kite
5 a) 360° b) 360° c) 360°
   d) 360° e) 540° f) 720°
   g) 360° h) 1080° i) 360°
6 a) triangle b) pentagon
   c) quadrilateral d) hexagon

25 Circles

1 $x = 44°$ (angle at centre)
2 $x = 152°$ (angle at centre)
3 $x = 32°$ (angle at centre)
4 $x = 32°$ (angle in same segment),
     $y = 28°$ (angle in same segment)
5 $x = 41°$ (angle in same segment),
     $y = 73°$ (angle in same segment)
6 $x = 55°$ (angle in same segment),
     $y = 55°$ (isosceles), $z = 55°$ (angle
     in same segment)
7 $x = 29°$ (angle in same segment),
     $y = 43°$ (angle in same segment)
8 $x = 26°$ (angle in same segment),
     $y = 87°$ (angles in triangle),
     $z = 87°$ (angle in same segment)
9 $x = 64°$ (isosceles triangle),
     $y = 32°$ (angle at centre)

10 $x = 62°$ (angle at centre),
      $y = 59°$ (isosceles triangle)
11 $x = 54°$ (angle at centre),
      $y = 63°$ (isosceles triangle),
      $z = 27°$ (isosceles triangle)
12 $w = 61°$ (angle in same segment),
      $x = 122°$ (angle at centre),
      $y = 58°$ (angles on straight line),
      $z = 29°$ (angle at centre)
13 $x = 70°$ (angle at centre)
      $y = 110°$ (opposite angles in cyclic
      quadrilateral)
14 $x = 160°$ (angles at point)
      $y = 80°$ (angle at centre)
15 $x = 150°$ (angles at point; angle at
      centre)
16 $w = 200°$ (angles at point)
      $x = 100°$ (angle at centre)
      $y = 50°$ (angles quadrilateral)
      $y = 80°$ (angle at centre OR opposite
      angles in cyclic quadrilateral)
17 $w = 85°$ (angles on a line)
      $x = 30°$ (angles in same segment)
      $y = 95°$ (opposite angles in cyclic
      quadrilateral)
      $z = 55°$ (angles in triangle)
18 $x = 35°$ (angles in same segment)
      $y = 55°$ (angles in semi-circle)
19 $x = 61°$ (angles in semi-circle)
      $y = 61°$ (angles in same segment)
20 $x = 66°$ (angles in semi-circle and
      angles in same segment)
21 $x = 108°$ (angles on a line)
      $y = 27°$ (angles in same segment)
      $z = 45°$ (angles in same segment)

26 Similar shapes

1 12 m
2 8 cm × 10 cm
3 16 cm
4 15 mm × 21 mm
5 a) $k = \frac{6}{5}$ b) $x = 14.4$ cm
6 c) $k = \frac{5}{4}$ d) $x = 10$ cm
7 16 cm × 20 cm
8 c) $\frac{x}{6} = \frac{10}{8}$
      d) $x = 7.5$ cm e) $y = 4.5$ cm
9 2.5 cm
10 a) CBD c) 12.5 cm d) 15 cm
11 3.6 cm
12 1:5 000 000
13 200 000 km²
14 75 cm²
15 1.61 m

16 9 cm
17 a) 16.6 kg b) 2560 cm²
18 33.0 m²

27 Geometrical constructions

1

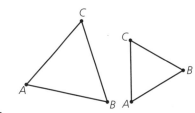

2

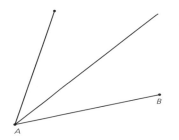

3

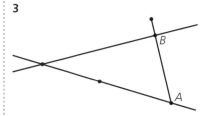

4 a)-d)

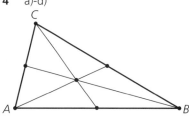

5 a)-d)

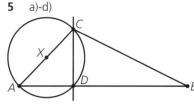

   e) C and D

28 Symmetry

1 a)

b) i) 2   ii) 1

   iii) 3   iv) 2

   v) 2   vi) 1

   vii) 1   viii) 1

2 a) 4

   b) 4

3

	Other vertices	Lines of symmetry
a)	(1, 3)	$y = 2$
b)	(10, 1) (10, 9)	$x = 8$, $y = 5$
c)	n/a	$x = 4$
d)	(0, 9)	$y = 7$ only
e)	(−2, 2)	$y = x + 3$
f)	(6, −4)	$x = 4.5$ only
g)	(−9, −6), (−1, 0) or (−3, −6)	None
h)	(−5, 1) (−7, 1)	$y = x + 8$ $x = −6$ $y = −4 − x$ $y = 2$

4 a) i)

   ii)

   b) 3   c) 7   d) 6

29 Locus

1 a) Circle, radius 4 cm, centre A

   b) 2 parallel lines (parallel to AB), 2 cm from AB with the same length as AB along with two semicircles centre A and B.

   c) A line perpendicular to CB and through the midpoint of CD.

   d) A line which bisects the angle BAC and goes through A.

2

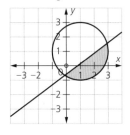

3

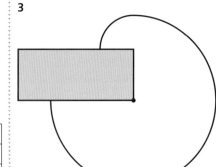

   b) 62.0 m²

4 a) & b)

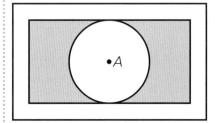

   c)

   d) 1940 m²   e) 383 m

5 c) A quarter circle, radius 1 m, whose centre is the corner of the wall and the floor.

6

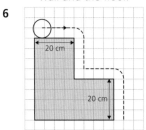

30 Mensuration

1 a) $x = 8$ cm   96 cm²

   b) $x = 5$ cm   75 cm²

   c) $x = 15$ cm   176 cm²

   d) $x = 9$ mm   126 mm²

2 24π

3 −

4 13 cm

5 a) $160 + 48\pi$ b) $160 + 60\pi$

   c) $960 + 324\pi$

6 60 cm³

7 8.06 mm

8 67

9 1.09 m

10 7.98 cm

11 b) 3.90 m²   c) 0.815 m²

   d) 815 m³   e) 15.7 m   f) 1570 m²

12 a) 0.66 m²   b) 264 m³

   c) Volume 47.5 m³   d) 120 m³

31 Trigonometry

1 365 mm

2 63.6 m

3 1803 m

4 6.93 cm

5 b) 67°

   c) 312 cm²

6 b) 26°

   c) 101°

7 a) 3.18 cm

   b) 3.12 cm

   c) −

8 a) 86.9 km²   b) 16 min

9 a) 33.8 cm   b) 164 cm²

   c) 18.1°, 88.9°   d) 350 cm²

10 a) 10.6 cm   c) 46.0°

32 Statistics

1 Positive correlation

2

a) Mean 5   Mode 3   Median 3   Range 12

b) Mean 22.3   Mode 22   Median 22   Range 23

c) Mean 1.1   Median 1.06   Range 0.34

d) Mean 8   Mode 13   Median 9   Range 12

e) Mean 47   Mode 51   Median 47   Range 11

f) Mean 113   Mode 119   Median 113   Range 17

g) Mean 88   Mode 88   Median 88   Range 14

3 a) 1.6 and 1.06

   b) Mean increased but median unchanged.

4 a) 3.51   b) 3

   c) Mode is 3 and range is 5

5 a) 42.5 kg

   b)

Weight, x (kg)	42.5	47.5	52.5	57.5	62.5	67.5
Frequency	43	31	39	28	19	15

   c) 523 kg

   b) "50-"

6 a)

Time taken, (x min)	57	62	67	72	77	82
Frequency	21	17	22	16	13	11

   b) 67.8 min

7 (20,0), (25,8), (30,29), (35,57), (40,76), (45,91), (50,100)

8 a) 65– b) 0 c) 79
 d) 64.8 kg

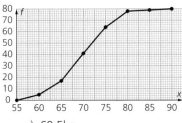

 e) 69.5 kg

9 a)

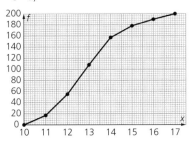

 b) 12.8 mm
 c) 11.9 mm and 13.7 mm

10 a)

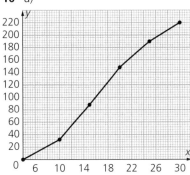

 b) 16.8 min
 c) 20.1 min
 d) About 125 candidates

11 a) 0.3
 b)

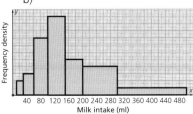

 c) & d)

Milk intake (ml)	10-	30-	60-	100-
No. of students	4	9	32	55
FD.	0.2	0.3	0.8	1.1

150-	200-	300-500
25	30	20
0.5	0.3	0.1

12 a)

Price of goods (£)	Frequency	Frequency Density
20 < x ≤ 40	20	1
40 < x ≤ 50	37	3.7
50 < x ≤ 60	62	6.2
60 < x ≤ 70	51	5.1
70 < x ≤ 90	30	1.5
90 < x ≤ 130	8	0.2

 b)

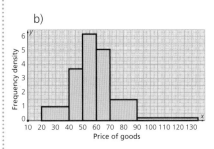

13 a)

Mass (kg)	Frequency	Frequency Density	Width on Histogram (cm)
10-	8	0.4	2
30-	16	0.8	2
50-	38	3.8	1
60-	40	4	1
70-	28	5.6	0.5
75-	30	6	0.5
80-	21	4.2	0.5
85-	11	2.2	0.5
90-120	6	0.2	3

 b)

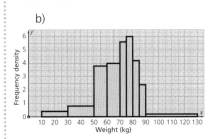

33 Probability

1 a) $\frac{9}{49}$ b) $\frac{24}{49}$
 c) $\frac{1}{7}$ d) $\frac{11}{49}$

2 a) $\frac{1}{4}$ b) $\frac{1}{12}$
 c) $\frac{2}{3}$ d) $\frac{7}{12}$

3 a) 2p, 3p, 4p b) 0.1 c) 0.6

4 a) 0.15 b) 0.4 c) 0.55

5 4

6 a) 100 b) 200 c) 100

7 130

8 a) 0.2 b) 0.1 c) 0.9 d) 0.75

9 a) $\frac{1}{3}$ b) $\frac{5}{6}$

10 a) .45 b) 0.6 c) 132

11 a) Independent
 b)

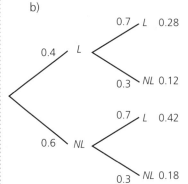

 c) 0.28 d) 0.54

12 a) $\frac{7}{72}$ b) $\frac{1}{16}$ c) $\frac{1}{12}$

13 a) HHH HHT HTH HTT THH
  THT TTH TTT
 b) i) $\frac{1}{8}$ ii) $\frac{1}{4}$ iii) $\frac{3}{8}$ iv) $\frac{7}{8}$

14 a) 2p b) -
 c) i) $\frac{4}{9}$ ii) $\frac{2}{9}$ iii) $\frac{1}{9}$

15 a) 64 b) $\frac{1}{64}$

16 a)

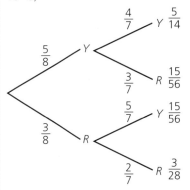

 b) i) $^3/_{28}$ ii) $^{13}/_{28}$
  iii) $^5/_7$

17 a)

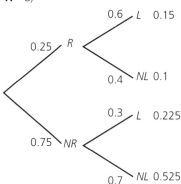

 b) i) 0.15 ii) 0.375 iii) 0.7

18 $^1/_2$

34 Vectors

1 a) $\begin{pmatrix} 2 \\ 14 \end{pmatrix}$ b) $\begin{pmatrix} -1 \\ 10 \end{pmatrix}$ c) $\begin{pmatrix} 3 \\ 4 \end{pmatrix}$

d) $\begin{pmatrix} -5 \\ 33 \end{pmatrix}$

2 a) $-\mathbf{p}$ b) $\mathbf{q}$ c) $\mathbf{p} + \mathbf{q}$ d) $\frac{1}{2}\mathbf{p}$

e) $\frac{1}{2}(\mathbf{p} + \mathbf{q})$ f) $\frac{2}{3}(\mathbf{p} + \mathbf{q})$

3 a) i) $\overrightarrow{AM} = \frac{1}{2}\mathbf{q}$ ii) $\overrightarrow{AN} = \frac{1}{2}\mathbf{p}$

iii) $\overrightarrow{AC} = \mathbf{p} + \mathbf{q}$

iv) $\overrightarrow{AR} = \frac{1}{4}(\mathbf{p} + \mathbf{q})$

v) $\overrightarrow{MR} = \frac{1}{4}(\mathbf{p} - \mathbf{q})$

vi) $\overrightarrow{RN} = \frac{1}{4}(\mathbf{p} - \mathbf{q})$

b) $\overrightarrow{MN} = \overrightarrow{RN}$

c) 1:2

4 a) i) $\mathbf{q} - \mathbf{p}$ ii) $\frac{1}{2}(\mathbf{q} - \mathbf{p})$

iii) $\frac{1}{2}\mathbf{p}$ iv) $\frac{1}{2}\mathbf{q}$

v) $\frac{1}{2}(\mathbf{q} - \mathbf{p})$ vi) $-\frac{1}{2}\mathbf{p}$

vii) $\frac{1}{2}\mathbf{q}$ viii) $\frac{1}{2}(\mathbf{q} - \mathbf{p})$

b) $\overrightarrow{BC} = 2\overrightarrow{XZ}$ c) 1:2

5 a) i) $\mathbf{s} - \mathbf{r}$ ii) $\mathbf{s} + \mathbf{r}$

iii) $\frac{2}{3}(\mathbf{s} - \mathbf{r})$ iv) $\frac{1}{3}2(\mathbf{s} + \mathbf{r})$

v) $\frac{1}{3}\mathbf{s}$ vi) $\frac{1}{3}(\mathbf{r} + \mathbf{s})$

b) $\overrightarrow{YX} = \frac{1}{3}\overrightarrow{AC}$ c) 1:3

35 Matrices

1 $x = 2, y = -1, z = 4$

2 a) $\begin{pmatrix} 7 & 18 \\ 5 & 13 \end{pmatrix}$ b) $\begin{pmatrix} -5 & -15 \\ -4 & -11 \end{pmatrix}$

c) $\begin{pmatrix} 9 & 6 \\ 31 & 35 \end{pmatrix}$ d) $\begin{pmatrix} 33 & 89 \\ 23 & 62 \end{pmatrix}$

e) $\begin{pmatrix} 34 & 83 \\ 25 & 61 \end{pmatrix}$ f) $\begin{pmatrix} 24 & 65 \\ 55 & 149 \end{pmatrix}$

3 a) 4 b) $\frac{1}{10}\begin{pmatrix} 6 & -2 \\ -10 & 5 \end{pmatrix}$

4 $x = 7, y = 21$

5 a) $\mathbf{A}^{-1} = \frac{1}{8}\begin{pmatrix} 4 & -6 \\ -2 & 5 \end{pmatrix}$

b) $\mathbf{B}^{-1} = \begin{pmatrix} -9 & 4 \\ 7 & -3 \end{pmatrix}$

c) $\mathbf{B}^{-1}\mathbf{A}^{-1} = \frac{1}{8}\begin{pmatrix} -44 & 74 \\ 34 & -57 \end{pmatrix}$

d) $\mathbf{A}^{-1}\mathbf{B}^{-1} = \frac{1}{8}\begin{pmatrix} -78 & 34 \\ 53 & -23 \end{pmatrix}$

e) $(\mathbf{AB})^{-1} = \frac{1}{8}\begin{pmatrix} -44 & 74 \\ 34 & -57 \end{pmatrix}$

f) $(\mathbf{BA})^{-1} = \frac{1}{8}\begin{pmatrix} -78 & 34 \\ 53 & -23 \end{pmatrix}$

6 $x = \frac{8}{3}$

36 Transformations

1 a) Reflection in the line $x = -1$

b) Enlargement of scale factor 2, centre (7, 6)

c) Enlargement of scale factor -2, centre $(-6, 0)$

d) Reflection in the line $y = -2$

2

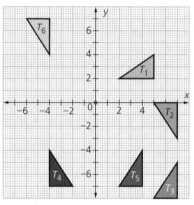

e) $\begin{pmatrix} -11 \\ 7 \end{pmatrix}$

3

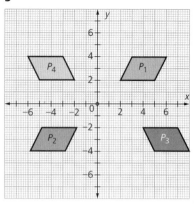

d) $\begin{pmatrix} -10 \\ 6 \end{pmatrix}$ e) $(-6, 4)$ f) $(-2, 2)$

4

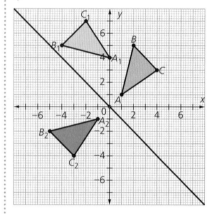

5 a) reflection in the x-axis

b) rotation of 90° anticlockwise

c) a reflection in $y = -x$

6 a) $\begin{pmatrix} -1 & 0 \\ 0 & -1 \end{pmatrix}$

b) $\begin{pmatrix} 2 & 0 \\ 0 & 2 \end{pmatrix}$